CANCER AND CLINICAL   Y

Teach thy tongue to say 'I do not know'
and thou shalt progress.

*from frontispiece to 'Retrolental Fibroplasia
a Modern Parable' by W. A. Silverman*

CLINICAL BIOCHEMISTRY IN MEDICINE SERIES

Series Editors: Gwyn McCreanor BSc, MSc, PhD, MRCPath
William Marshall MA, PhD, FRCP, FRCPath

Cancer and Clinical Biochemistry

Peter Pannall, MB BCh, FFPath (SA), FRCPath(UK), FRCPA, FAACB

Senior Director, Clinical Chemistry, The Queen Elizabeth Hospital, Woodville, South Australia.
Clinical Senior Lecturer, University of Adelaide.

Dusan Kotasek, MB BS (Hons), FRACP

Senior Consultant Medical Oncologist, The Queen Elizabeth Hospital, Woodville, South Australia.

A C B V E N T U R E P U B L I C A T I O N S

with generous support from Abbott Diagnostics Division, EURO-DPC Ltd
and Boehringer Mannheim UK Ltd

ACB VENTURE PUBLICATIONS
Chairman and Managing Editor - David Burnett

CLINICAL BIOCHEMISTRY IN MEDICINE
Series Editors - Gwyn McCreanor and William Marshall

British Library Cataloguing in Publication Data

A catalogue record for the book is available from the British Library

ISBN 0 902429 09 4 ACB Venture Publications

Cover Design - Mark Howlett, The Image Foundry, Cambridge

Cover picture – *Cancer Pagurus, the Great Crab*

Printed by Piggott Printers (Cambridge) Ltd

Preface

The clinical biochemistry of cancer is fascinating for several reasons. The first is the range of biochemical abnormalities encountered, as malignancy may involve any organ. Some of these changes are produced directly while others relate to syndromes resulting from something the tumour produces. The recognition of such syndromes and research into their pathophysiology have lead to the identification of previously unknown molecules, such as parathyroid hormone-related protein, and expanded knowledge of normal physiology. There are several paraneoplastic syndromes still unexplained. Similarly, the search (so far in vain) for molecules specific for, and so diagnostic of, malignancy has expanded understanding of the structure of the normal cell. Finally, with advances in molecular techniques, studies on malignant cells have complemented and enhanced knowledge of how cells grow and function.

The subjects covered in this book may seem to stray beyond the traditional boundaries of clinical biochemistry. This is intentional as we believe it is important to have an overview of the extent, and limitations, of existing knowledge of the disease. We have therefore begun with a consideration, albeit superficial, of why a cell becomes malignant and why tumours spread. While at present this is largely of interest only, it is likely that the future will see routine laboratories examining tumour cells to look for markers that may predict behaviour. Similarly, while the clinical biochemist's involvement in therapy may currently centre largely on monitoring response and detecting complications, it is important to see this in the overall context and to appreciate the reasoning behind the many therapeutic measures, if for no other reason than to be aware of the problems facing the oncologist.

In addition to these topics, we consider the changes that may occur in the 'routine' biochemical tests. These are mostly non-specific but may produce the occasional startling result and patterns of changes that may suggest the presence of malignancy and provide information about its nature and extent. The tests that have acquired the status of 'tumour markers' are considered in some detail, with emphasis on their appropriate use and limitations. Work in this area has also contributed significantly to understanding of the normal cell. More importantly, it has shown that the natural history of some tumours is poorly understood. As detection of early cancers, or precancerous lesions, improves, it will become important to distinguish those which are likely to progress and spread from those which will probably not do so. If there is an answer to this question it may lie in the identification of genetic changes that free the cell from its normal constraints.

There are many unanswered questions but they are being asked. Clinical biochemists should be aware of the developing opportunities and be prepared to offer tests that prove to be of clinical value. We hope that this book will contribute to a deeper understanding of malignancy.

Our thanks are due to the many people who have read parts of the book or made useful comments, in particular Alex Dobrovic, Dusan Veljkovic, and Jeffrey Crocker. We are also deeply grateful to Mrs Wendy Holdback for superb secretarial assistance and facing revision after revision with a smile.

July 1997
Peter Pannall and Dusan Kotasek

ACKNOWLEDGEMENTS

The authors are grateful to the following for permission to reproduce or adapt material for certain figures used in this text.

Cain H J, Pannall P R, Kotasek D, Norman R J. Choriogonadotrophin-mediated thyrotoxicosis in man. *Clin Chem* 1991; **37:** 1127-1131 (Figure 5.8)

Fearon E R, Molecular genetics of colorectal cancer. *Ann N Y Acad Sci* 1995; **768:** 101-110 (Figure 1.5)

Pannall P. The clinical biochemistry of malignancy. *Clin Biochem Revs* 1992; **13:** 142-152 (Figures 2.9, 2.10 and 4.7)

Contents

Chapter 1

The Nature Of Malignancy

There are many different types of cancers, all characterised by continuing proliferation of cells and by impairment of cellular differentiation. This chapter will consider the mechanisms of the changes that occur in the cell and how such cells form a tumour which may ultimately spread to other parts of the body.

THE CANCER CELL

Early workers investigated the biochemistry of the malignant cell to see how it deviated from normal, and possibly to explain its behaviour. With hindsight this was unrewarding. It was noted that tumour cells had a high rate of glycolysis, now known to be due to overexpression of the enzyme hexokinase in malignant cells, and that they produced lactate even in the presence of oxygen. Enzymes involved in growth (anabolism) were found to be present at greater activities than those involved in catabolism. It is now believed that this and other changes identified are a feature of rapid cell growth, benign or malignant, rather than the cause of such growth. Another characteristic noted was the production of proteins in forms that resembled those of the fetus. As these are expressed only slightly, if at all, in the normal adult cell, they are called oncofetal proteins. This is seen in the fetal isoenzyme patterns in several enzymes of intermediary metabolism, and in the re-expression of growth factors, polypeptide hormones and of cell surface molecules such as carcinoembryonic antigen. These differences may influence the behaviour of the cell and its relation to other cells, as well as forming the basis of many tumour marker assays.

It is now apparent that the abnormality of the malignant cell lies at a more fundamental level – in the genes that control cell growth and communication. Cancer develops as a result of multiple genetic alterations, occurring over a long period of time, which disrupt the cell cycle, differentiation and growth control.

Many tumours originate from rapidly renewing cell populations, such as bone marrow and intestinal epithelial cells, while others arise from tissues that normally have slower rates of proliferation, but are induced to proliferate, often triggered by tissue injury, for example tobacco smoke in the lung. Tissue renewal in normal situations represents a balance between cell proliferation, differentiation and cell death. Stem cells represent a minute proportion of the total cell pool but have a crucial function of self-renewal and proliferation. Normal proliferation and differentiation is clearly different to neoplastic growth but in some ways tumours can be thought of as caricatures of normal tissue renewal. In neoplastic tissues, the proliferative response is irreversible and is inherited by subsequent generations of tumour cells. In some tumours relatively low rates of proliferation are accompanied by failure of the undifferentiated cells to undergo senescence and programmed cell death (apoptosis); this results in the accumulation of long-lived, abnormal tumour cells. To see these changes in perspective we will briefly outline the normal cell growth cycle.

THE CELL GROWTH CYCLE

All cells other than germ cells reproduce by mitosis, in which the genetic material in the chromosomes is duplicated and two daughter cells are formed, each with a full complement of chromosomes. The cell cycle (Figure 1.1) is divided into four phases:

- **M** phase (mitosis)   during which cell division occurs. It lasts 0.5 - 1 hours.
- **G₁** phase (gap 1)   during which the cell grows. Its length is variable.
- **S** phase (synthesis)   during which DNA copying and chromosome duplication occurs. It lasts 10 - 20 hours.
- **G₂** phase (gap 2)   preparation for mitosis, lasting 2 - 10 hours.

The G_1, S and G_2 phases are together called the interphase.

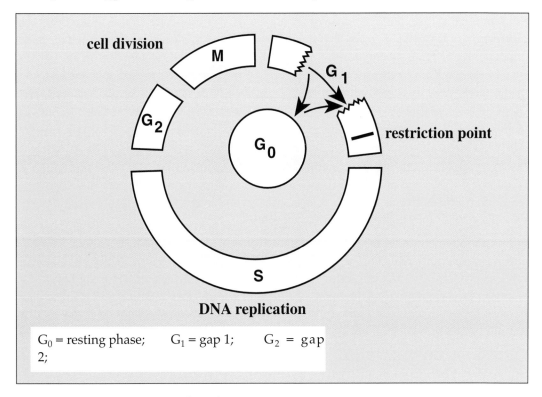

Figure 1.1   The cell growth cycle

After mitosis the daughter cells enter G_1, from which they may enter a resting phase, G_0, during which the cell functions but is removed from the growth cycle. This G_0 phase accounts for the great variations in the growth rates of different cell types. Some, such as the cells forming the epithelium of the gut, divide twice or more times a day while others, such as neurons, do not divide again once correct numbers have been reached. The G_0 phase varies also according to need; the cycle of the normal liver cell is a year or more but may be shortened to a day or so if replacement of damaged liver tissue is required. From G_0, cells may re-enter G_1 or pass into a cycle of programmed cell death.

One control point of the cycle lies in the G_1 phase and cells progress along, or re-enter the cycle from G_0, only in response to a stimulus. As this is the area most affected in the development of malignancy it will be described in greater detail, albeit in outline only (Figure 1.2). The interested reader is referred to the reviews in the further reading list.

The stimulus to growth is the binding of extracellular growth factors, often in combination, to specific receptors on the cell surface. Many of these are transmembrane tyrosine-specific protein kinases which relay the signal through a series of intracellular signalling proteins to reach the nucleus. Here, proteins that inhibit transcription are phosphorylated and inactivated resulting in gene induction. This occurs in two phases, early and late, with the products of the early response genes probably inducing late response genes. An important transcription inhibitor is the retinoblastoma protein, pRB (p. 9).

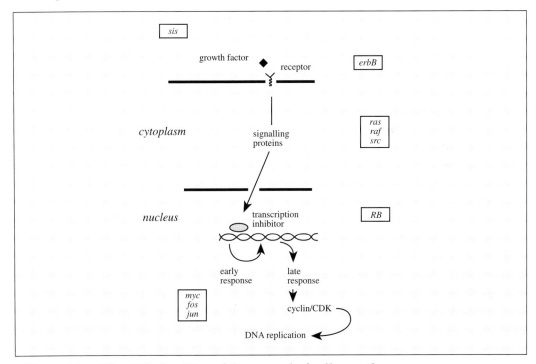

Figure 1.2   **Simplified outline of the control of cell growth**
Examples of genes that influence the various stages appear in boxes
Abnormalities of these are frequently found in malignancy

The ultimate trigger for passing into the S phase is a complex of molecules forming a restriction point control. Essential components of this control are the cyclin-dependent protein kinases (CDKs) which are regulated by binding to cyclins D, E, A and B, levels of which increase in that order as the cycle progresses. The cyclins are so named as there is cyclic activation and dissociation of the complexes. These molecules are late gene response products and rising concentrations set the cell inevitably along the path to division. Cyclin D1 is overexpressed in many human cancers due to gene amplifications.

Several inhibitors may act along this pathway. A family of polypeptides that inhibit CDK4, the INK4 proteins, can arrest the G_1 phase. Mutations of these have been found in several cancers. Other CDK inhibitors include the products of the p21, p27 and p57 genes. The p21 gene in turn is induced by the tumour suppressor p53 protein (see p. 9).

Other systems limit the life of any particular cell line and prevent the further growth of abnormal cells. For example:

- If the genetic material, the DNA, of a cell is damaged, the cell will not divide until the damage has been repaired. If it cannot be repaired, the cell dies by a process known as apoptosis. One of the main proteins involved in the decision to enter apoptosis is the p53 protein (p. 9). Abnormal p53 protein produced by tumours permits the continued replication of abnormal DNA and leads to chromosomal abnormalities which may further affect gene action.

- The telomere, a structure forming the end of each chromosome, is made up of a repeating DNA sequence formed by the enzyme telomerase. As cells age, the telomere shortens and this is thought to restrict the number of times a cell line can divide. In malignant cells telomerase renews the telomere much more effectively than in normal cells, rendering the cell line immortal.

- Cells require to attach to a basement membrane through adhesion molecules called integrins. If they do not, growth stops by inhibiting the cyclin E-CDK2 complex. This does not occur in malignant cells.

Alterations to any of the genes that control elements of this pathway may promote unrestricted cell growth by:

- excessive production or activity of growth factors;
- producing an abnormal receptor that signals even when growth factors are not present;
- excessive production or activity of the intracellular or nuclear signalling proteins;
- loss of inhibitory proteins at any of the many points at which they act.

More than one genetic event (probably 3 to 7) in the same cell is required to produce a malignant tumour. This is more likely to happen if the cell type is a rapidly dividing one, or is repeatedly exposed to a carcinogen. The need for more than one event also explains the relatively late age of onset of most cancers. If, however, a tumour-promoting genetic alteration is carried in the germline, and so is present in every cell of the body, fewer additional events are required and tumours may develop at an earlier age. While a number of hereditary cancer syndromes serve as examples, albeit rare, of this type, the majority of genetic alterations observed in human cancers are acquired. Tumour cells themselves have a high rate of mutation and the selection of subclones with a growth advantage leads to the evolution of tumours with even more malignant properties. Evolution of such heterogeneous subclones may be due to further mutations, differentiation within a clone, or variations in the nutritional environment of tumour cells.

It is likely that a cancer begins in a single cell, i.e. it is monoclonal. In some cases a unique identifying tumour marker (a clonal marker) may be identified in all the cells of the tumour. Clonal markers are a characteristic of many haematological malignancies such as lymphomas, leukaemias and myelomas and are used extensively in diagnosis. Molecular probes are used to detect unique genetic clonal markers such as oncogene point mutations, chromosomal rearrangements (e.g. the Philadelphia chromosome in chronic myeloid leukaemia) and deletions of tumour suppressor genes.

The discovery of the role played in cancer development by oncogenes and tumour suppressor genes over the past decade has greatly increased our understanding of cancers and has led to new diagnostic approaches. Therapeutic applications of these discoveries are entering the clinical arena (e.g. gene therapy trials) and will undoubtedly revolutionise future therapy of many of the common cancers.

GENES INVOLVED IN HUMAN CANCERS

The multistep process which results in the development of cancer is the consequence of genetic changes in the cell. Genes that participate in this neoplastic cell transformation fall into three broad categories, oncogenes, tumour suppressor genes and DNA repair genes.

ONCOGENES

Oncogenes are mutated forms of normal cellular genes called proto-oncogenes. Proto-oncogenes are genes which code for proteins that regulate normal cellular growth processes such as proliferation, differentiation and programmed cell death, and disruption of their normal function has profound consequences for the cell. Proto-oncogenes can be classified into five major groups based on the biochemical and functional properties of their protein products. These groups are:

- growth factors   e.g.   *sis*
- growth factor receptors   e.g.   *fms*

- signal transducers   e.g.   *src, ras*

- transcription factors   e.g.   *fos, jun, myc*

- programmed cell death regulators   e.g.   *bcl-2.*

Further examples of proto-oncogenes classified according to their functional categories appear in Figure 1.3.

Oncogenes act in an autosomal dominant fashion to promote tumour development through a gain-of-function mechanism. They were originally identified as the transforming genes of RNA tumour viruses. The discovery of the Rous sarcoma virus in 1911 by Peyton Rous suggested for the first time that an infectious agent was capable of inducing malignant transformation. Later research identified a number of other transforming genes in retroviruses that were capable of inducing tumours in animals such as the mouse, rat, cat and chicken. To date, more than a 100 different oncogenes have been discovered with the majority identified in experimental animal models of cancer. However only a relatively small number have been implicated in the initiation and progression of human cancers.

The activation of oncogenes involves genetic changes to the cellular proto-oncogene either by mutation, gene amplification or chromosomal rearrangement.

- Mutation (by a process of deletion, base substitution or insertion) typically results in structural alteration of the encoded protein, leading to uncontrolled and continuous activity. One of the commonest genetic lesions, seen in perhaps 10-20% of all human cancers, is the activation of the signal transducing functions of the ras protein, usually by a point mutation.

- Gene amplification results from the expansion in the number of copies of a gene. Gene amplification may sometimes be observed under the microscope as the extra copies of a gene are manifest in the cell's karyotype as double minute chromosomes, or homogeneous staining regions. Cells with extra copies of genes may have a selective growth advantage as a consequence of the increased gene expression.

Proto-oncogene	Function of protein product
Growth factors	
sis	Platelet-derived growth factor
int-2	Growth factor
Growth factor receptors	
erb B	Tyrosine kinase/EGF receptor
erb B-2	Tyrosine kinase
kit	Tyrosine kinase
fms	Tyrosine kinase/CSF1 receptor
met	Tyrosine kinase
trk	Tyrosine kinase
ret	Tyrosine kinase
ros	Tyrosine kinase
sea	Tyrosine kinase
mas	Angiotensin receptor
Signal transduction	
H-ras, K-ras, N-ras	binds GDP/GTP
src	Tyrosine kinase
abl	Tyrosine kinase
fes	Tyrosine kinase
fgr	Tyrosine kinase
lck	Tyrosine kinase
yes	Tyrosine kinase
raf	Serine/threonine kinase
pim	Serine/threonine kinase
mos	Serine/threonine kinase
gsp	G protein
gip	G protein
Transcription factors	
c-myc, L-myc, N-myc	DNA binding
fos	DNA binding/AP-1 complex with jun
jun	DNA binding/AP-1 complex with fos
erb A	DNA binding/T3 receptor
ets	DNA binding
rel	DNA binding
ski	DNA binding
myb	DNA binding
Programmed cell death regulation	
bcl-2	membrane protein/apoptosis

Figure 1.3   Proto-oncogenes and their products

- Chromosomal rearrangements are most frequently seen in haemato-logical malignancies such as leukaemias and lymphomas. These rearrangements are usually chromosomal translocations (movement of part of one chromosome to another) or chromosomal inversions that result in either fusion gene products or in a transcriptional activation of a proto-oncogene. For example, in Burkitt's lymphoma, the *c-myc* gene is translocated from its normal position on chromosome 8 to the immunoglobulin loci on chromosomes 2, 14 or 22 where it is activated by the immunoglobulin regulatory elements.

TUMOUR SUPPRESSOR GENES

Unlike oncogenes which harbour activating mutations, tumour suppressor genes are inactivated in human cancers. Most tumour suppressor genes function directly in cell growth regulation pathways and inactivating mutations lead to a selective growth advantage for the affected cells. The concept of tumour suppressor genes stems from observations that hybrid cells generated by the fusion of tumorigenic and non-tumorigenic cells are non-tumorigenic unless certain chromosomes are lost. Thus, the deletion of chromosomal material containing genes with an antiproliferative capacity may result in deregulation of growth and tumour generation. A large number of tumour suppressor genes are thought to exist but only a dozen or so have been identified so far. Identification of tumour suppressor genes has been difficult as these genes are manifest by their absence as opposed to oncogenes, the products of which are present in increased amounts. Consequently, identification has depended on the study of certain rare cancers, usually familial, the best example of which is retinoblastoma.

Retinoblastoma is a rare tumour of childhood, accounting for only 1% of childhood cancer deaths. The tumour involves the retina and can be unilateral or bilateral and multifocal; 40% of cases are familial. Knudson, based on his observation of the incidence and age of onset of unilateral and bilateral cases of familial retinoblastoma, postulated the existence of an inherited mutation in patients with familial retinoblastoma. This inherited mutation typically involves only one of the two alleles inherited from the parents, so is referred to as loss of heterozygosity. Such individuals require only one additional mutation for tumours to arise; in non-familial cases, two events, resulting in the inactivation or deletion of both normal alleles, are required. In other words, in the non-hereditary unilateral retinoblastomas, both mutations are somatic and must occur in the same cell. Given the low frequency of mutations and the gradual disappearance of the target cell from the retina, retinoblastoma is a very uncommon tumour. In the hereditary cases on the other hand, the first mutation exists in the germline, and so in every cell, and only one further mutation is required in any target cell to result in malignancy. Given the large number of target cells in the retina in childhood, the occurrence of a second mutation is almost guaranteed, thus resulting in a tumour, often more than one.

Chromosomal studies of retinoblastoma tumours have shown the presence of deletions in the region of chromosome 13q14; this region was subsequently shown to contain the *RB1* gene, abnormality of which confers susceptibility to retinoblastoma. The *RB1* gene encodes a nuclear phosphoprotein involved in cell cycle regulation, designated *pRB*. Inactivation of the *RB1* gene has been described in several cancers other than retinoblastoma. These include small cell lung cancer, carcinoid tumours and osteosarcoma.

The p53 tumour suppressor gene is one of the most intensively studied genes in human cancers. Because of its ability to monitor DNA damage and to promote the destruction of damaged cells, it has been dubbed the 'guardian of the genome'. p53 is the most commonly mutated gene in human cancer and germ line mutations of p53 have been linked to an inherited predisposition to a number of cancers (e.g. Li-Fraumeni syndrome, p. 15). The presence of increased amounts of cellular p53 has been associated with cell cycle arrest and apoptosis, while mutations of the p53 gene are associated with instability of the genome.

The p53 gene encodes a protein with a molecular weight of 53 kD, hence its name, which functions as a transcription factor and suppresses the growth of cells which have damaged DNA. It appears to do this by activating a number of genes such as that of the p21 protein which inhibits phosphorylation of proteins such as pRB. p53 mutations result in a p53 protein that is incapable of DNA binding or of activating gene transcription.

The high prevalence of p53 mutations in human cancers suggests that it could be used as a marker of human malignancy. Such mutations occur both early (cancer of the lung, head and neck, and breast) and late (gastrointestinal, prostate, ovarian, bladder, cervical, endometrial and liver cancers) during tumour development. The mutations can be detected by amplification of DNA and RNA using the polymerase chain reaction (PCR), followed by direct sequencing, or by immunohistochemistry to detect increased amounts of the protein in tumour tissue. Immunohistochemical techniques are based on the fact that wild type p53 protein has a tissue half-life of only a few minutes, whereas the mutant p53 typically has a half life of several hours. Consequently, tissues containing mutant p53 will show prominent nuclear immunostaining compared to normal tissues in which this is either absent or at virtually undetectable levels. The presence of the p53 mutation has been associated with aggressive tumour behaviour and worse prognosis in some tumour types. In many, but not all tumours, p53 mutation is an independent prognostic marker (colorectal cancer, soft tissue sarcomas, gastric cancer, non-small cell lung cancer).

Another tumour suppressor gene that has received a lot of publicity is the gene BRCA1 which occurs in about half the families with familial breast cancer. In these families ovarian cancer is also common. Early figures suggested that the chance of carriers of the BRCA1 gene developing breast and ovarian cancer was 85% and 50% respectively. This may not apply to all families as the degree of penetrance may vary. A second gene BRCA2 has been found in other families with breast cancer.

Several of the heritable cancer syndromes have chromosomal deletions or loss of heterozygosity, suggesting that the tumours arise at least in part after the loss of a tumour suppressor gene. Non-familial cancers of the same type may arise by a similar mechanism, but require loss or mutation of both normal alleles, mutation of one allele and the loss of the other allele or mutation of one allele so it acts as a dominant-negative mutation to incapacitate the function of the normal allele. A list of some of these tumours is found in Figure 1.4.

Tumour	Site of allele loss (gene)
Osteosarcoma	13q (RB1)
Retinoblastoma	13q (RB1)
Wilms' tumour	11p13 (WT1), 11p15 (WT2)
Renal cell carcinoma	3p (VHL),17p
Bladder (transitional cell)	11p, 17p (p53), 9p (CDKN2), 9q
Hepatocellular carcinoma	11p
Hepatoblastoma	11p15
Rhabdomyosarcoma	11p15, 17p13 (p53)
Lung: small cell carcinoma	3p,13q (RB1),17p
Breast carcinoma	11p,11q,13q,16q (E-cadherin), 17p (p53)
Breast, ovarian carcinoma	17q21 (BRCA1)
Breast carcinoma	13q (BRCA2)
Stomach carcinoma	13q, 5q (APC)
Pancreatic carcinoma	18q (DPC4)
Colorectal carcinoma	5q (APC),17p (p53),18q (DCC), 1p, 8p
Insulinoma	11
Phaeochromocytoma	1p, 22
Medullary thyroid carcinoma	1p
Meningioma, ependymoma, Schwannoma	22q (NF2)
Neurofibroma, phaeochromocytoma	17q (NF1)
Melanoma	9p (CDKN2), 17q (NF1)
Prostate	8p

Figure 1.4   Tumours in which there is loss of a tumour suppressor gene

DNA REPAIR GENES

These genes recognise and repair damaged DNA. They were first implicated as cause of human disease by the study of rare syndromes with autosomal recessive inheritance (xeroderma pigmentosum, Bloom syndrome and ataxia telangiectasia, p. 14). More recently, DNA repair defects have also been implicated in cancer predisposition syndromes with an autosomal dominant mode of inheritance. The best example is the hereditary non-polyposis colorectal cancer syndrome (HNPCC), in which germ line mutations in any of at least four DNA repair genes, hMSH2, hMHL1, hPMS1 and hPMS2, have been identified. The normal cells of patients with HNPCC can repair DNA because they retain one copy of the gene inherited from the non-affected parent. However, a somatic mutation may inactivate this remaining wild-type allele; when this occurs mismatch repair becomes deficient and mutations begin to accumulate at a rapid rate.

The development of cancer through a multistep process of genetic alterations is perhaps best exemplified by the genetic model of Fearon and Vogelstein for colorectal carcinoma where the progression from benign to malignant histology is well understood (Figure 1.5). The genetic changes demonstrate the complex interplay of tumour suppressor genes, oncogenes and DNA mismatch repair genes during the progression, over years or even decades, from benign adenoma to carcinoma. Most tumours are thought to arise by the gradual accumulation of such genetic events with the accumulation of mutations, rather than their chronological order, being the most important factor.

THE MALIGNANT TUMOUR

Cancers are a biologically heterogeneous group, comprising many types of malignant neoplastic growths. Tumours that arise from epidermal tissues (e.g. skin, glandular epithelium) are carcinomas while tumours that arise from mesenchymal tissues (e.g. bone, cartilage, muscle) are sarcomas. Tumours arising from the haematopoietic cells of the bone marrow are termed leukaemias, while those derived from lymphoid tissues such as lymph nodes or spleen are referred to as lymphomas. The pathological description usually refers to tumours as well-differentiated, poorly-differentiated or anaplastic according to the tumour's ability to maintain a semblance of differentiation; anaplastic tumours typically behave in a more aggressive fashion than their more well differentiated relatives.

As discussed above, continuing genetic change within the growing cancer produces numerous cell subpopulations which may differ in many ways. In general the cells become more abnormal and, possibly only after multiple changes, some acquire the ability to become invasive. A uniform characteristic of malignant neoplasms is this ability to invade host tissues and result in metastases. At the time of diagnosis, approximately 30% of patients with solid tumours will already harbour clinically detectable metastases and a further 30% will have clinically occult micrometastases which will become manifest over time. The ability of the cells of a cancer to metastasise represents its most malignant characteristic and is responsible for the majority of cancer deaths.

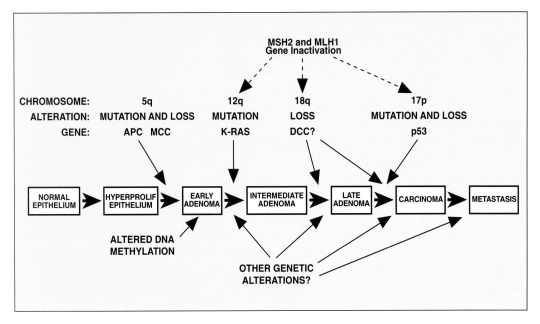

Figure 1.5   A genetic model of colorectal cancer showing the inherited and acquired genetic alterations found at various stages in the progression from normal mucosa, through adenoma to carcinoma. It is thought that inactivation of the DNA damage recognition and repair genes MSH2 and MSH1 may lead to more rapid acquisition of other gene mutations, not necessarily in the order shown in the model

(Reproduced with permission from Fearon ER. Molecular genetics of colorectal cancer. Ann NY Acad Sci 1995;768:101-110.)

INVASION, ANGIOGENESIS AND METASTASIS

Tumours may spread directly through adjacent tissue or along surfaces such as the peritoneum. Cells may also enter lymphatic vessels and travel to the lymph nodes draining that region. Most importantly, spread may occur through the bloodstream from the primary tumour or lymph node secondaries, to establish secondary tumour deposits (metastases) in distant sites. The clinical significance of this is that cure by local treatment alone is no longer possible, and more toxic systemic therapy is necessary.

The processes which ultimately lead to the formation of metastases depend on both host and tumour-related factors. The factors that influence tumour proliferation, invasion and metastasis can exert their effects in both a positive and negative manner. The process is highly complex and involves a sequence of events.

- Tumour growth and vascularisation (see below).

- Separation from other cells.
  Successful metastasis also involves changes in adhesion proteins, groups of cell surface molecules such as the cadherins (intercellular adhesion), integrins (attachment to extracellular matrix), selectins, CD44 and the immunoglobulin superfamily (which includes carcinoembryonic antigen). It is necessary for the malignant cell initially to release itself from neighbouring cells and basement membrane, and later to adhere to the capillary endothelium in the organ in which the metastasis develops. The role of adhesion proteins is under intense study. Cadherins have been noted to be absent or abnormal in malignant cells.

- Cleavage of basement membrane and extracellular matrix.

- Entry into a blood (or lymphatic) vessel.
  Cancer cells (and normal white blood cells) achieve this by increasing the activity of enzymes such as metalloproteinases, serine proteases (e.g. tissue plasminogen activator and urokinase) and cysteine proteases (cathepsin D) which dissolve membranes. Activities of these enzymes correlate with invasiveness and propensity for metastasis. There are endogenous inhibitors to these proteases which, if their activity is low, would enhance spread. One such inhibitor, maspin, is expressed less frequently in advanced breast cancer than in early tumours.

- Spread through the bloodstream.
  Once cells are present in the bloodstream, metastasis is still not assured; most cells die quickly. Recent techniques for the detection of circulating cancer cells have shown that they are relatively easily detected.

- Trapping in the capillaries of a distant organ.
  For most tumours, the first capillary bed encountered is that of the

lungs, whereas for intestinal tumours it is usually the liver. It is not well understood why certain tumours develop secondaries in particular organs: it is presumed that factors in the host tissue attract, or favour the growth of, the malignant cells.

- Penetration and growth in that organ. This uses the same mechanisms as in the first two steps.

Angiogenesis, the process of new blood vessel formation, is a prerequisite for the local growth of tumour colonies beyond a size (about 2mm) to which they are restricted by oxygen and nutrient diffusion. Such new blood vessels are crucial to the continued growth of the tumour and to the further spread of cancer cells through the vasculature as these newly formed blood vessels are relatively easily penetrated by malignant cells. The process of angiogenesis is similar to cellular invasion, with the events of adhesion, proteolysis and migration that characterise the spreading of cancer cells also being displayed by the endothelial cells. Tumour cells produce several endothelial mitogens such as basic fibroblast growth factor (bFGF), vascular endothelial growth factor (VEGF) and platelet-derived endothelial cell growth factor (PD-ECGF) which result in growth of new blood vessels and so further tumour growth. Endothelial cells in the tumour vascular bed then produce factors that can stimulate proliferation or motility of tumour cells; these include platelet-derived growth factor (PDGF), insulin-like growth factor 1 (IGF-1), bFGF, heparin-binding epithelial growth factor (HB-EGF), granulocyte-colony stimulating factor (G-CSF) and interleukin-6.

Understanding the process of metastasis may improve ways of predicting the behaviour of a particular tumour and offer a new range of therapeutic options. Such intervention, targeting endothelial cells in the tumour bed using monoclonal antibodies and angiostatic agents, is beginning to enter clinical trials; early studies demonstrate that combinations of chemotherapeutic agents and angiogenesis inhibitors are more effective than either treatment alone.

FAMILIAL CANCER SYNDROMES

Several syndromes, referred to above, result from the presence of a defective gene in the germ line. Some are uncommon but they are dramatic and include the following:

Ataxia telangiectasia is dominated by progressive cerebellar ataxia and telangiectasia (vascular malformations) of the eyes and skin. These patients also have immune and endocrine abnormalities and a greatly increased risk of lymphoma as well as a greater risk of breast and other cancers. The defect is in a DNA repair gene.

Bloom syndrome is characterised by an increased frequency of leukaemia and character-istic cytological abnormalities. It too is due to a defective DNA repair gene.

In the **Li-Fraumeni syndrome**, tumours, often multiple, develop by young adulthood. The commonest is breast cancer followed by leukaemia, brain tumours, and sarcoma of bone and soft tissues, as well as adrenocortical carcinoma. Other tumours may develop later in life. The defect is a germ line p53 mutation.

Xeroderma pigmentosum is characterised by severe photosensitivity to sunlight and a high incidence of skin cancer. There may also be neurological abnormalities. The defect is in a DNA repair gene.

Familial adenomatous polyposis is a condition characterised by the development of many colorectal adenomatous polyps early in life and a very high risk of colorectal cancer. There is a germ line mutation of the APC (adenomatous polyposis coli) gene on chromosome 5q. This syndrome accounts for less than 1% of colorectal cancers but somatic mutation of the APC gene is found in the majority of sporadic cancers and adenomas of the colon.

Hereditary non-polyposis colorectal cancer accounts for 5 - 10% of colorectal cancer cases. The germline mutation affects one of the DNA repair genes and somatic mutation of the normal allele results in a decreased ability to repair DNA mismatches that may arise in a dividing cell.

The familial syndromes that clinical biochemists are most likely to encounter are the **multiple endocrine neoplasias** (MEN). This term describes inherited syndromes in which particular tumours, usually benign, develop in more than one endocrine organ. The importance lies in recognising that more than one endocrine tumour may be present in a patient, and in investigating the family when necessary. There are three groups (Figure 1.6), inherited in an autosomal dominant manner.

The tumours of multiple endocrine neoplasia			
	MEN 1	**MEN 2A**	**MEN 2B**
Pituitary adenoma	50		
Parathyroid adenoma/hyperplasia	90	30	
Pancreatic islet cell tumour	50		
Medullary carcinoma of the thyroid		100	100
Phaeochromocytoma		50	50
Ganglioneuroma			100
The figures are the average percentage frequencies in the respective syndromes.			

Figure 1.6   The tumours of multiple endocrine neoplasia

MEN 1, also known as Wermer's syndrome, is characterised by parathyroid chief cell hyperplasia that progresses to adenoma formation. Hypercalcaemia usually develops before the age of 40 years and the diagnosis is made as for sporadic hyperparathyroidism. Any of the islet cell tumours (p. 97) may develop but the commonest is gastrinoma, more than half of which are malignant. The commonest pituitary adenoma is a prolactinoma. The gene for MEN 1 has been located to chromosome 11 (11q13) and probably codes for a tumour suppressor protein.

MEN 2, also known as Sipple's syndrome, is dominated by the development in all patients of medullary carcinoma of the thyroid (p. 71). Early diagnosis by screening family members greatly improves the prognosis for this malignancy. About half the patients also develop phaeochromocytoma (p. 73) and also benefit from early diagnosis. A proportion of patients with MEN 2A also develop hyperparathyroidism. MEN 2B patients have a characteristic long and lanky appearance, called marfanoid (as in Marfan's syndrome) and have ganglioneuromas, tumours of the nervous system. The gene for MEN 2 is on chromosome 10 (10q11.2) and has been identified as the *c-ret* proto-oncogene which codes for a receptor tyrosine kinase. Most affected individuals have point mutations in exon 10 or 11 (MEN 2A) or exon 16 (MEN 2B). Assays of peripheral blood cells for the DNA abnormality found in an affected family identifies those members as risk.

THE ROLE OF THE CLINICAL LABORATORY

The tools of molecular biology are increasingly available in the routine laboratory and the opportunity exists for detecting many of the genes discussed above. The ability to measure something does not however, mean that it should be measured.

The possible reasons for doing so are as follows:

- **evaluation of risk**
  In families with one of the heritable cancer genes, identification of those at risk is important if early treatment would be of benefit. This is clearly the case in the MEN 2 families. In other instances it is less so. BRCA 1 mutations (p. 9) are associated with an increased risk of breast and ovarian cancer, but the risk appears to vary between different families and mutations are detected in only about half the families with familial breast cancer. This uncertainty applies also to the other markers. At present they should be used only in a research setting with appropriate support services.

- **early diagnosis of cancer**
  Mutant p53 and/or *ras* oncogenes have been found in preparations from easily obtained samples such as urine, faeces and sputum in patients with cancers of the bladder, colon and lung respectively. These changes are likely to be present at an early stage but the rates of false positive and false negative results have not been established. As

described in this chapter, many gene changes are needed to produce an invasive tumour. Experience with plasma tumour markers has shown that findings in one situation are not necessarily applicable to another. Before these tests are used for clinical purposes they must be properly evaluated.

- **prognosis and staging**
  Identification and detection of the gene changes that correlate with invasiveness and the ability to metastasise may one day be of value in practice, if it can be used to predict the likely behaviour of the tumour and particularly if advances in therapy allow targeting of specific functions. There have been many attempts to detect and quantitate tumour cells in the peripheral blood. The most sensitive method is reverse transcriptase-PCR which detects the mRNA of a selected marker such as prostate specific antigen. This has not yet been adopted into staging protocols because of the uncertain significance of the finding.

In summary, molecular biology techniques have greatly increased knowledge about the nature of malignancy. The transfer of any of this knowledge to the clinical laboratory for use on patients requires thorough evaluation of the relevant test and its interpretation. Moreover, the result should be clinically relevant. Tests that meet these criteria would be welcome additions to the laboratory repertoire.

FURTHER READING

Aaronson S A. Growth factors and cancer. *Science* 1991; **254:** 1146-1153.

Berges R, Isaacs J T. Programming events in the regulation of cell proliferation and death. *Clin Chem* 1993; **39:** 356-361.

Duffy M J. The biochemistry of metastasis. *Adv Clin Chem* 1996; **32:** 135-166.

Duffy M J. Can molecular markers now be used for early diagnosis of malignancy? *Clin Chem* 1995; **41:** 1410-1413.

Fearon E R. Molecular genetics of colorectal cancer. *Ann NY Acad Sc* 1995; **768:** 101-110.

Fearon E R, Vogelstein B. A genetic model for colorectal tumorigenesis. *Cell* 1990; **61:** 759-767.

Fidler I J. Cancer metastasis. *Br Med Bull* 1991; **47:** 157-177.

Liotta L A. Cancer cell invasion and metastasis. *Scientific American* 1992; **266(2):** 34-41.

Pelkey T J, Frierson (Jr) H F, Bruns D E. Molecular and immunological detection of circulating tumour cells and micrometastases from solid tumours. *Clin Chem* 1996; **42:** 1369-1381.

Ruoslahti E. How cancer spreads. *Scientific American* 1996; **275(3):** 42-47.

Schmandt R, Mills G B. Genomic components of carcinogenesis. *Clin Chem* 1993; **39:** 2375-2385.

Sherr C J. Cancer cell cycles. *Science* 1996; **274:** 1672-1677.

Velculescu V E, El-Deiry W S. Biological and clinical importance of the p53 tumour suppressor gene. *Clin Chem* 1996; **42:** 858-868.

Weinberg R A. How cancer arises. *Scientific American* 1996; **275(3):** 32-40.

Weinberg R A. Tumor suppressor genes. *Science* 1991; **254:** 1138-1146.

Chapter 2

Biochemical Effects Of Tumour Growth

In patients with cancer many different factors may produce organ dysfunction or abnormal biochemical results. For example, impaired renal function may result from:

- fluid losses   - vomiting, diarrhoea, diuresis
- hypercalcaemia   - humoral or local mechanisms
- hyperuricaemia   - tumour destruction
- protein deposition   - Bence Jones protein
- glomerular or tubular damage   - chemotherapy
- outflow obstruction   - tumour growth.

Similarly, an abnormal result such as hyponatraemia may result from:

- sodium losses   - fluid losses
                                             - adrenal destruction
- water retention   - tumour ADH secretion
                                             - chemotherapy
- pseudohyponatraemia   - myeloma with hyperproteinaemia.

Most of these changes are non-specific, but interpreted with the knowledge of the clinical situation, many are of use in diagnosis, prognosis and management. The progress of a tumour is often monitored using one or more selected tumour markers but routine biochemical tests may provide similar information and are of particular value in detecting spread to other organs.

Biochemical changes may result from:

- the physical effects of the tumour (primary or secondary) or the host tissue reaction to it;

- the metabolic activity of the tumour;

- substances produced by the tumour;

- the non-specific systemic response to tissue damage;

- chemotherapy.

PHYSICAL EFFECTS OF TUMOURS

Tumours may produce obstruction, tissue damage and bleeding or exudation depending on the site of growth.

OBSTRUCTION

A tumour may obstruct any duct or hollow organ, such as:

- The bile duct, resulting in obstructive jaundice with hyperbilirubinaemia and elevated plasma alkaline phosphatase (ALP) and gamma glutamyltransferase (GGT) activities. This is seen in patients with carcinoma of the head of the pancreas or with involvement of lymph nodes in the porta hepatis; Figure 2.1 shows a case of bile duct obstruction.

- The bowel, resulting in intestinal obstruction and possible fluid and electrolyte disturbances.

- The urethra, both ureters or the bladder neck resulting in renal failure with all its attendant biochemical changes.

Obstruction of other sites such as the oesophagus or bronchus may ultimately lead to malnutrition or respiratory failure respectively but initially do not produce biochemical changes.

TISSUE OR ORGAN DESTRUCTION

The destruction of normal tissue by tumour, or areas of necrosis in the tumour itself, results in the release of cell contents such as enzymes. Plasma lactate dehydrogenase (LD) and aspartate transaminase (AST) activities may rise but often the destruction is gradual and so the changes are minimal. Complete destruction of an organ may lead to loss of function. This is seen most often when small organs, such as endocrine glands, are involved. Examples include:

- **Hypopituitarism** due to destruction of the anterior gland or pituitary stalk. This is rare but may be caused by a primary pituitary tumour (usually benign) or a secondary deposit, often from breast or lung carcinoma. Symptoms usually only develop after 75% of the gland is destroyed.

- **Diabetes insipidus** from pituitary stalk or hypothalamic involvement.

- **Hypoadrenalism** due to bilateral adrenal destruction, usually by secondary tumour, particularly from breast or lung cancer. While the adrenal is a common site for metastases which usually involve both glands, destruction to the point of hypofunction is less common.

Bile duct obstruction

This 68 year old woman was told by a friend that she looked yellow. On checking in the mirror she found this was indeed so, and she went to her general practitioner who referred her to hospital.

On examination she was clearly jaundiced but, other than an enlarged liver, there were no abnormal physical findings. A blood test showed:

Plasma				
	Bilirubin	232	µmol/L	(1 - 20)
	Albumin	31	g/L	(33 - 50)
	ALP	1896	U/L	(35 -100)
	GGT	1082	U/L	(0 - 70)
	AST	355	U/L	(0 - 45)

This is a predominantly cholestatic pattern. Cholangiography showed a grossly dilated biliary system with narrowing of the bile duct where it entered the duodenum. At laparotomy, carcinoma of the head of the pancreas was found. A bypass procedure (choledochoduodenostomy) was performed to re-establish biliary drainage into the gut (↓ in the graph below).

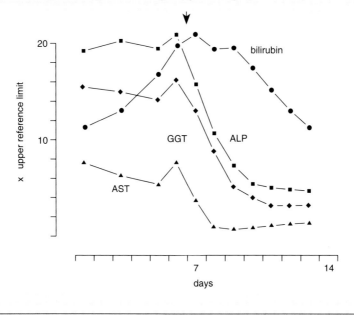

Figure 2.1   **Bile duct obstruction. Figures in brackets are reference intervals**

LIVER INVOLVEMENT

The liver is a frequent site of secondary tumours, particularly of the gastrointestinal tract via the portal venous system. Clinically there is often pain and enlargement of the liver and, with extensive involvement, jaundice. Isolated liver metastases may be amenable to surgical removal.

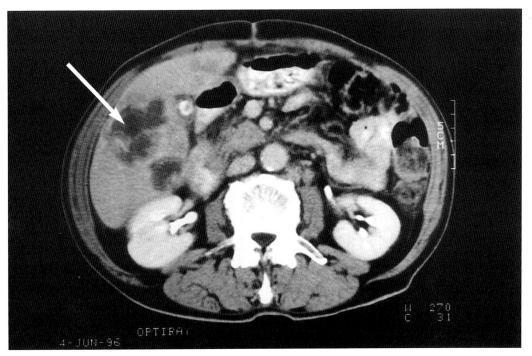

Figure 2.2   A CT scan of the abdomen showing secondary tumour in the liver

Malignancy, primary or secondary, may be present in the liver without any abnormality of plasma 'liver function tests'. In other cases there may be mild to moderate increases in plasma transaminase activity, particularly AST. A particularly significant finding is that of cholestasis, denoted by elevated plasma ALP and GGT, with minimal or no increase in plasma bilirubin. This indicates infiltration or focal lesions in the liver producing local areas of obstruction to bile flow, but leaving other areas unaffected. These unaffected areas allow excretion of bilirubin but this will not affect the raised enzyme levels as they are not normally excreted by the liver.

While this pattern may occur with benign conditions such as granulomatous disease, it is more commonly due to secondary tumour. A similar pattern of cholestasis, often with mild jaundice, is described in patients with renal carcinoma, apparently without liver involvement by tumour, and may revert to normal after nephrectomy. The mechanism is unknown.

Chemotherapy may also cause liver damage or cholestasis and must be considered as a possible cause of any abnormality.

BONE INVOLVEMENT

Bone is another common site of metastasis. The bones of the axial skeleton (spine, ribs and pelvis) are most commonly involved as they contain red marrow and have a rich blood supply (Figure 2.3). The tumours that most often metastasise to bone are those of the breast, prostate, lung, kidney, thyroid and gastrointestinal tract.

Secondary tumour in bone leads to bone destruction which manifests as pain and is one of the most disturbing aspects of disseminated malignancy. The weakened bone may fracture easily (pathological fracture), particularly in sites of weight bearing such as the neck of the femur.

Collapse of involved vertebrae may compress nerves or the spinal cord. The destruction is due to osteoclast activation by tumour, or host tissue derived, cytokines, particularly interleukin 6 (IL-6), interleukin 1 (IL-1) and tumour necrosis factor alpha (TNF-α). There may also be local production of PTHrP (p. 83), particularly by secondaries from breast cancer. The bone loss provokes an osteoblastic response with increased plasma ALP activity; this varies from a marked response with very high ALP (breast and prostate secondaries) to predominantly lytic lesions as in myeloma when the plasma ALP is usually normal, unless repair of a fracture is occurring (Figure. 2.5). With extensive osteolytic lesions hypercalcaemia may develop. This is discussed further in Chapter 5.

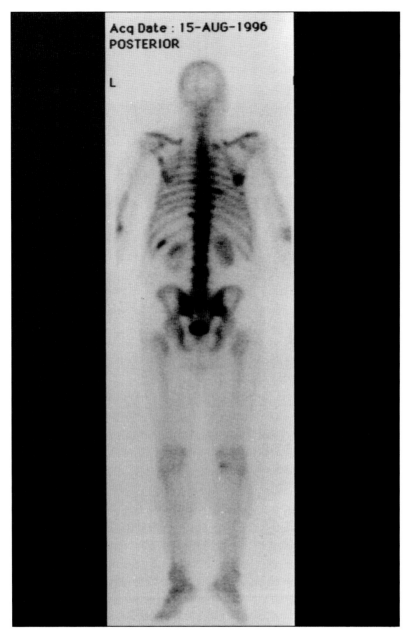

Figure 2.3 A bone scan of a patient with disseminated prostate cancer showing the axial distribution of the metastases (dark areas). Technetium 99m-labelled MDP (methylene diphosphonate) is injected and taken up in areas of increased osteoblastic activity where, as it is a gamma-emitter, it is detectable by a gamma camera. This test is very sensitive for bone secondaries but is not specific as the MDP can also collect at sites of inflammation. The dark spot in the pelvis is excreted MDP in the bladder

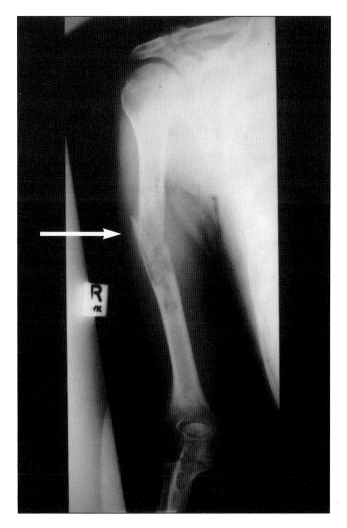

Figure 2.4 **An Xray showing a fracture of the humerus at a site weakened by a secondary deposit from breast cancer**

Administration of osteoclast-inhibiting drugs such as the bisphosphonates may lessen the severity of the bone destruction, relieving pain and reducing the risk of fracture. Sites of symptomatic bone secondaries may be treated with radiotherapy to relieve pain.

Specific assays of bone ALP may detect increases while the total ALP is normal, as may other markers of bone breakdown, such as urinary pyridinium cross links. There is currently no clinical benefit from such early detection.

Primary bone tumours, such as osteogenic sarcoma, may also cause an increased plasma ALP but this finding does not contribute to management.

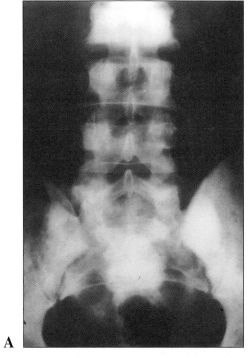

A

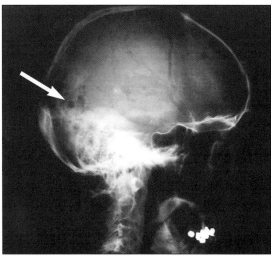

B

Figure. 2.5   These two Xrays show the extremes of osteoblastic reaction, and
therefore plasma alkaline phosphatase activity, in bone secondaries

A - dense, sclerotic secondaries in a patient with prostate cancer.
The plasma ALP was 2152 U/L (35 - 115 U/L).
B - lytic deposits in a patient with myeloma.
The plasma ALP was 92 U/L.

NERVOUS SYSTEM INVOLVEMENT

The brain and spinal cord may be involved by primary or secondary malignancy. Destruction or pressure on these structures or on spinal nerves may produce a range of neurological symptoms. The diagnosis is usually made by imaging techniques but cerebrospinal fluid (CSF) is often submitted for biochemical testing. The changes, if present, are non-diagnostic but the most constant abnormality is a moderately raised CSF protein concentration due to bleeding or exudation from the tumour.

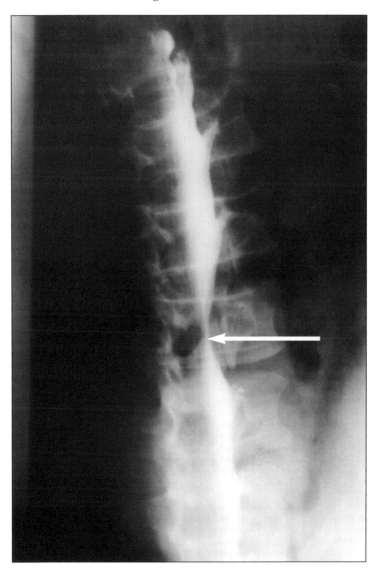

Figure. 2.6   This contrast-enhanced Xray shows obstruction of the spinal canal by a tumour, in this case a secondary deposit from a melanoma

Very high concentrations (10 - 20 g/L) (Figure 2.7) may be noted if a tumour in the spinal canal (Figure. 2.6) obstructs the normal circulation of the CSF and leads to pooling and concentration, and the lumbar puncture is below the site of obstruction. The fluid may appear yellow (xanthochromia).

Site	Above	Below
Appearance	Clear	Yellow
Protein (g/L)	0.31	37
Glucose (mmol/L)	1.4	1.4

Cerebrospinal fluid taken from above and below
the site of a tumour blocking the spinal canal

Figure. 2.7   Spinal canal obstruction

Diffuse spread of tumour over the meningeal membranes (meningeal carcinomatosis) may occur in patients with lymphoma or leukaemia, or from carcinoma of the breast or lung. Cytological examination of the CSF is of greatest value. Biochemical changes resemble those of meningitis with raised protein and low glucose concentrations due to the metabolism of the tumour cells. A range of other abnormalities, such as elevation of the enzyme beta glucuronidase, has been described but probably offer little to the clinical evaluation.

Some tumour markers such as human chorionic gonadotrophin (HCG) may be measured in CSF to detect secondary involvement.

EXUDATION AND BLEEDING

Fluid collections, such as pleural effusion in the chest or ascites in the abdomen, may be transudates, due to venous back pressure, or exudates, due to involvement of the surface lining by disease. The two can usually be distinguished by the protein content which is low in transudation and high (> 30 g/L) in exudation, and by the clinical findings. Malignancy is an important cause of exudation but biochemical analysis offers little to distinguish it from benign causes such as inflammation. In both, lactate dehydrogenase activity may be high and glucose concentrations low.

Bleeding may be an early manifestation of gastrointestinal or urinary tract cancers and is often sought in a patient presenting with iron deficiency anaemia. Consequently the detection of blood in the urine or faeces is an important part of diagnosis and follow-up.

Normal subjects lose about 1.5 mL of blood into the gastrointestinal tract each day (about 2 mg Hb/g faeces), an amount not usually detected by tests for occult blood in faeces. Abnormal bleeding may occur from any site from the stomach to the rectum. In the gut the haemoglobin is progressively degraded, resulting in the destruction of globin and modification of the haem to a range of haem-derived porphyrins. This has some relevance to the selection of tests for the detection of faecal occult blood. There are three groups:

- Immunochemical tests that detect only the intact human haemoglobin molecule. This is usually still present in the faecal sample only when the source of bleeding is in the colon or rectum; positive results are highly specific for the site but not, of course, for the cause. Samples should be analysed without undue delay to avoid further degradation.

- Tests using guaiac which detects the peroxidase activity of intact haem, i.e. haem that still contains iron. These detect bleeding from both upper and lower gastrointestinal tract. They are not specific for human haemoglobin, so it may be necessary to check positive results after instituting a meat-free diet for a few days. However, plant peroxidases may also give a positive result and ascorbic acid may produce false negative results.

- Tests detecting haem-derived porphyrins also detect blood from the upper and lower gastrointestinal tract. They too are not specific for human haemoglobin but are not affected by plant peroxidases.

Cancers bleed variably and intermittently so several specimens should be tested and samples should be taken from the surface of the stool where blood is more likely to be present. It is essential to follow the manufacturer's instructions on sample collection and test performance. Haemoglobin in specimens collected and dried on the paper slides provided is more stable than that in a lump of faeces in a container.

EVIDENCE OF GROWTH AND CELL TURNOVER

Most of the biochemical changes described above are due to physical factors and may be produced by benign or malignant processes. Certain changes however, indicate greatly increased cellular activity or rapid cell growth and so suggest malignancy. These are seen most often in patients with leukaemias, lymphomas and small cell cancer of the lung where there is rapid cell growth and a large tumour burden. The significant findings are:

- Raised plasma urate, not due to renal impairment. Urate is produced by the breakdown of nucleic acids and high concentrations are noted in malignancies with high cell turnover. The hyperuricaemia rarely produces clinical gout but the urate may precipitate in the renal tubules and cause renal failure. Very high concentrations may also result from destruction of cells by chemotherapy, (see tumour lysis syndrome p. 116) so xanthine oxidase inhibitors are given to inhibit urate production and prevent renal damage.

Lymphoma

This 53 year old male presented with general malaise and upper abdominal pain. His liver and spleen were enlarged.

Plasma				
	Creatinine	110	µmol/L	(50 - 120)
	Urea	6.3	mmol/L	(3.0 - 7.6)
	Urate	0.79	mmol/L	(0.15 - 0.50)
	Calcium	2.35	mmol/L	(2.10 - 2.60)
	Phosphate	1.21	mmol/L	(0.70 - 1.30)
	Albumin	35	g/L	(33 - 50)
	Globulins	24	g/L	(24 - 42)
	Bilirubin	14	µmol/L	(1 - 20)
	ALP	338	U/L	(35 -100)
	AST	88	U/L	(0 - 45)
	GGT	370	U/L	(0 - 70)
	LD	2040	U/L	(120 - 250)

Note:

1. **Hyperuricaemia**, with no evidence of renal impairment, and very high LD activity. Together these suggest increased cell turnover. The LD isoenzyme pattern was non-specific with mainly LD_2 and LD_3 increased.

2. **Cholestasis** (increased ALP and GGT) **without jaundice** suggesting focal liver involvement or infiltration.

   The mildly elevated AST could be from liver or the malignant cells.

   These results indicate a large tumour burden, the sort of case in which there is a risk of developing tumour lysis syndrome on treatment.

Figure 2.8   Lymphoma. Figures in brackets are reference intervals

- Plasma lactate dehydrogenase activity is increased in many malignancies and this should be considered in any patient with a high and otherwise unexplained LD result. Mild to moderate increases probably reflect tissue destruction but very high levels (5 to 10 times normal) may be seen in patients with lymphoma or leukaemia and in certain cancers of the ovary or testis. Other solid tumours may occasionally be associated with very high LD activities, probably as a direct result of production of the enzyme. The isoenzyme profile is most commonly a non-specific one with increases in LD_2 and LD_3. Ovarian and testicular cancers however, often have increases in LD_1 and LD_2, with LD_1 greater than LD_2 (the myocardial pattern). Less commonly a tumour may produce predominantly LD_5.

Leukaemia and lactate dehydrogenase

Results on a patient with leukaemia showing the relationship between plasma LD and tumour burden as reflected by the total white cell count. While LD estimation is clearly superfluous in this case, it is of value in patients with lymphoma and other rapidly growing tumours which do not have the direct marker of the white cell count.

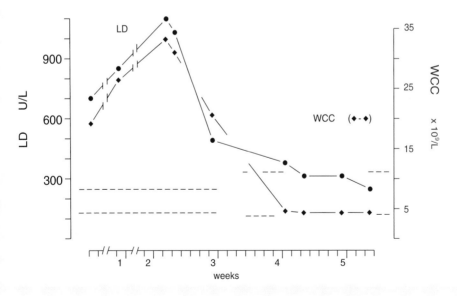

The horizontal broken lines indicate the reference intervals.

Figure 2.9   Leukaemia and lactate dehydrogenase

In patients on chemotherapy who are also receiving granulocyte colony stimulating factor (G-CSF see p. 109), plasma LD activity may rise in parallel with the white cell count and should not be taken as evidence of worsening malignancy. In some patients a similar rise in ALP has been noted.

- Malignant cells have a high rate of glycolysis but much of the pyruvate produced is converted to lactate. This is usually taken up by the liver and reconverted to glucose but infrequently, lactic acidosis develops.

Lactic acidosis

This 32 year old man presented in lactic acidosis after a short history of weight loss and general malaise. He was found to have a lymphoma.

No other cause for the lactic acidosis was present. As shown below, the acidosis settled as he entered chemotherapy-induced remission, and recurred with relapse. The LD is a marker of tumour mass and the two arrow heads indicate the beginning of courses of chemotherapy.

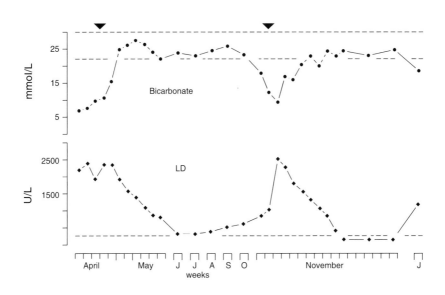

The horizontal broken lines indicate the reference interval for plasma bicarbonate and the upper reference limit for LD.

Figure 2.10   Lactic acidosis

These changes are seen in an exaggerated form in the syndrome of tumour lysis, most often a complication of instituting chemotherapy. This is considered further in Chapter 6.

Artefactual hyperkalaemia may be a problem in samples from patients with leukaemia and very high white cell counts (>100 000 x 10^9/L). Destruction of these cells during venepuncture, and particularly during centrifugation of the sample, results in release of potassium into the plasma. This may be minimised if the specimens are identified and centrifuged at a slower speed, or potassium is measured on the uncentrifuged sample by ion-selective electrode.

Artefactual hyperkalaemia

This 61 year old woman had chronic lymphatic leukaemia. The high plasma potassium on 13 February caused some concern but the result from a repeat sample (*), centrifuged slowly, was reassuring. In patients with extremely high leucocyte or platelet counts, normal centrifugation can disrupt cells and artefactually increase plasma potassium levels.

Date	28 Jan	13 Feb	13 Feb*	20 Feb	3 Mar
Plasma potassium (mmol/L)	5.0	9.2	5.0	5.0	4.8
Leucocyte count (x 10^9/L)	68	192		84	71

Figure 2.11   Artefactual hyperkalaemia

TUMOUR PRODUCTS

Tumours may produce a range of molecules that may be typical to the cell involved, or may be apparently unrelated. These may be hormones or cytokines that produce clinical syndromes, the paraneoplastic syndromes (Chapter 5). Another group comprises the tumour markers (Chapters 3 and 4) which are of value in assessment and monitoring. There is some overlap between these categories. In addition, tumours occasionally produce other substances, often enzymes, which may serve as markers in a particular case but which are too infrequently to be of general value.

- **Lactate dehydrogenase** as a marker of cell proliferation and as a marker of ovarian and testicular tumours, has been discussed. Some solid tumours, such as lung, colon and stomach, may occasionally be associated with very high plasma LD levels.

- **Alkaline phosphatase** is a particularly useful enzyme in following patients with malignancy as it may detect secondary involvement of bone or liver. A form of ALP similar (98% sequence homology) to that produced by the placenta is secreted by certain tumours. This is placental-like alkaline phosphatase (PLAP) and is normally expressed at low levels in lung and testis. It is also known as germ cell ALP. Raised plasma activities (often with normal total ALP activity) have been described in carcinoma of the lung, seminoma of the testis and some gynaecological cancers, especially serous adenocarcinoma of the ovary. It is measured immunochemically. Several less well defined ALP variants have also been described in patients with a range of cancers.

- **Creatine kinase BB** may be produced by tumours of the neuroendocrine system or tumours showing neuroendocrine differentiation. Small cell carcinoma of the lung and prostate cancer are most commonly involved. Total CK activity is not commonly raised but assays for CK-MB will show high values if the assay does not distinguish between CK-MB and CK-BB.

- **Hyperamylasaemia** of the S-type has been described in a range of tumours.

- **Muramidase** (lysozyme) is an enzyme secreted by myelomonocytic cells. In myelomonocytic leukaemia, plasma levels may be very high. The enzyme may damage the proximal renal tubule and cause reduced reabsorption of potassium and magnesium with hypokalaemia and hypomagnesaemia. As magnesium is required for the secretion and action of parathyroid hormone, severe hypomagnesaemia may result in hypocalcaemia. This combination of low plasma potassium, calcium and magnesium may also occur as a complication of chemotherapy (p. 107).

Renal tubular damage and magnesium loss

A 72 year old man went to his doctor because he was feeling tired. Tests showed **acute leukaemia** so he was referred to hospital. On admission the following results were noted.

Plasma			
	Sodium	144 mmol/L	(135 - 144)
	Potassium	2.4 mmol/L	(3.5 - 4.8)
	Bicarbonate	31 mmol/L	(22 - 30)
	Chloride	99 mmol/L	(94 - 106)
	Creatinine	110 µmol/L	(50 - 120)
	Calcium	1.54 mmol/L	(2.10 - 2.60)
	Phosphate	1.02 mmol/L	(0.70 - 1.30)
	Albumin	35 g/L	(33 - 50)

Hypokalaemic alkalosis and hypocalcaemia are an uncommon combination. When present, hypomagnesaemia should be considered.

	Magnesium	0.36 mmol/L	(0.75 - 1.15)
	PTH	4.7 U/L	(1 - 6)

After restoration of normal plasma magnesium, by infusion beginning at (↓) PTH secretion increased and corrected the hypocalcaemia.

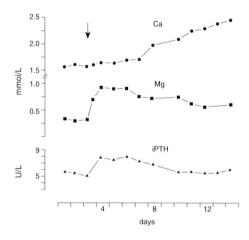

The cause of the hypomagnesaemia was urinary loss of magnesium due to proximal renal tubule damage by high levels of muramidase (lysozyme) from the leukaemic cells. Serum muramidase was 138 mg/L (3 - 9).

Figure 2.12   Renal tubular damage and magnesium loss. Figures in brackets are reference intervals

TISSUE RESPONSE TO INJURY

Malignancy is one cause of the tissue damage that evokes the acute phase response. This is mediated by cytokines, particularly IL-6, TNFα and IL-1 from host tissue and, in some cases, from tumour tissue. The changes are non-specific and should be recognised as such, even though they may be used in prognosis. Several studies have shown that patients in whom these changes persist after treatment do worse than those in whom the abnormalities return to normal. This presumably reflects residual tumour. The most marked expression of this response is the cachexia that afflicts some patients.

The changes may be summarised as:

- **Acute phase proteins**
  Plasma concentrations of several proteins such as alpha-1-antitrypsin, haptoglobin, caeruloplasmin, fibrinogen and complement component C3 as well as C-reactive protein, may be increased. The concentrations of other proteins such as albumin and transferrin fall. Ferritin, the iron storage protein, is also an acute phase reactant and elevated plasma concentrations occur in a range of conditions. Very high concentrations may be associated with a number of tumour types such as those of lung and kidney.

- **Trace metals**
  Plasma zinc concentrations are often low due to increased urinary excretion of the element. Plasma iron is also low but the association with low transferrin and high ferritin concentrations shows this to be part of the acute phase response, not iron deficiency. Plasma copper concentrations are raised due to the increase in caeruloplasmin and this has been used to monitor some tumours such as lymphoma.

- **Lipids**
  A range of plasma lipid changes has been described in malignancy. The most constant change is a low plasma cholesterol. Hypercholesterolaemia that returns to normal after therapy has been described in patients with hepatocellular carcinoma. The mechanism is not known. Moderate increases in plasma cholesterol have also been noted in patients after cisplatin chemotherapy for germ cell tumours.

CANCER CACHEXIA

About one in five patients with malignancy develops progressive weight loss, anorexia and general debilitation that reduces the ability to respond to infections, reduces the efficacy of chemotherapy and shortens life. These patients, in addition to losing weight, have hypoalbuminaemia that may lead to oedema, and are often anaemic. While it may be due partly to reduced intake of food, nutritional support does not usually reverse it.

Non-specific changes in serum cholesterol

This 77 year old man had multiple myeloma and chemotherapy had controlled the disease for several years. The paraprotein concentrations in his final two years are shown below and illustrate the fall in plasma cholesterol that occurs as the malignancy worsens.

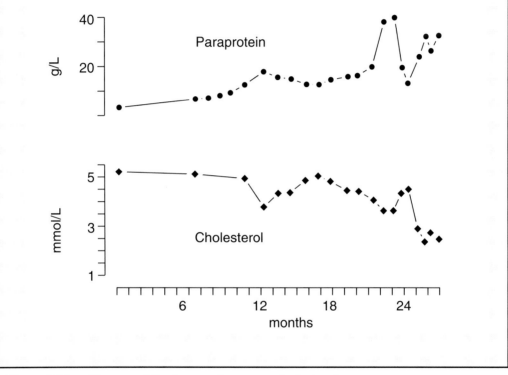

Figure 2.13   Non-specific changes in serum cholesterol

Patients suffering from cancer cachexia have been shown to have a particular metabolic pattern, one similar to that once seen in chronic infections such as tuberculosis, and to the catabolic states of sepsis and trauma. The abnormalities are:

- increased   -   glycolysis
                      -     lipolysis
                      -     protein catabolism

- insulin resistance

- anaemia

- hypoalbuminaemia.

It is a hypermetabolic state rather than the hypometabolic response to starvation. There is both loss of fat and muscle wasting with increased breakdown of fat and oxidation of fatty acids. As in starvation, the body shifts from carbohydrate-based to fat-based fuel. Unlike starvation however, ketosis is uncommon. Glucose intolerance is an early feature. Later gluconeogenesis increases, fueled largely by lactate from the tumour. Many tumours obtain energy by glycolysis with lactate as the end product. This is converted to glucose in the liver, a process that consumes more energy than is gained from glycolysis and results in an energy loss to the host. This may be an important factor in the negative energy balance. Increased muscle catabolism contributes aminoacids for gluconeogenesis.

The pathogenesis is not completely understood. It is not related to tumour size and it is probable that factors released from host tissue in response to the tumour mediate the metabolic changes. The most likely factors are cytokines; TNFα, interferon gamma, IL-1 and IL-6 have been implicated. TNFα can increase gluconeogenesis and also increases glucagon levels. Experimentally these cytokines can produce the clinical syndrome of cancer cachexia and it is likely that their actions overlap or potentiate one another. However, some animal models of cancer cachexia have demonstrated the presence of a transferable plasma factor distinct from those mentioned.

Treatment of cancer cachexia is difficult. Enteral or parenteral feeding is not particularly successful. One promising agent is the progestational drug, megestrol acetate, which improves appetite and promotes weight gain, mainly fat.

FURTHER READING

Burgeois S M, Rofe A M, Conyers R A J, Coyle P, Bais R. Cancer cachexia: metabolic and hormonal changes in the host. *Clin Biochem Revs* 1992; **13:** 152-160.

Ellis M J C. Metastatic bone disease and the role of bisphosphonates. *Br J Hosp Med* 1996; **56:** 339-345.

Pannall P. The clinical biochemistry of malignancy. *Clin Biochem Revs* 1992; **13:** 142-151.

Young G P, St John D J B. Faecal occult blood tests: choice, usage and clinical applications. *Cin Biochem Revs* 1992; **13:** 161-169.

Chapter 3

Tumours and Tumour Markers – General Considerations

As discussed in Chapter 2, routine biochemical tests provide valuable information in patients with malignancy. The term 'tumour marker' however, is more commonly applied to something that is measured in tissue or body fluids in order to detect malignancy and possibly to define the organ involved, as well as to establish the extent of tumour burden before treatment and to monitor the response to therapy. This chapter will consider what these markers are, and their uses and limitations while Chapter 4 will consider their application in specific situations. Only the most frequently used markers are discussed in detail; others are mentioned to put them in perspective.

THE NATURE OF TUMOUR MARKERS

Almost anything that forms part of a malignant cell or that is produced by that cell may, in certain situations, be useful as a marker. The main groups are:

- structural molecules;
- secretion products and enzymes;
- non-specific markers of cell turnover.

It must be stressed that all these markers have their counterparts in non-malignant cells and that while there are some qualitative differences, current assays do not distinguish malignant from benign cell proliferation. Results must always be considered in the over-all clinical context.

In addition to these there are cellular markers such as the amount of DNA (ploidy) in the cell, the percentage of cells in the proliferation phase of the cell growth cycle and the presence of oncogenes or their products. While helping to characterise malignancy they are not in common use as tumour markers.

STRUCTURAL MOLECULES

Many tumour marker assays detect epitopes on structural molecules, most commonly these found on the cell surface. These are common to many epithelial cells and so are of little value in identifying the tumour type. The first was carcinoembryonic antigen and the story of its development illustrates the problems.

CARCINOEMBYRONIC ANTIGEN

In 1964 Gold and Friedman produced an antibody that detected a 'tumour-specific' antigen in human colon cancers. They did this by raising antibodies to extracts of colon cancer tissue, subsequently removing normal antigens by adsorption with normal colon extracts from the same specimens. What was left was an antibody, or antibodies, that detected something present in malignant, but not in normal tissue. As the antigen was found to be present in neoplastic tissue and in the embryonal gastrointestinal tract it was named carcinoembryonic antigen (CEA). This was the first of the 'designed' tumour markers. It was later identified as a highly glycosylated cell surface glycoprotein involved in intercellular adhesion. Its size varies in different organs from 90 - 200kD, due to variable glycosylation.

In 1969 a radioimmunoassay for CEA in serum was described. Initially CEA was believed to be a specific, but not a sensitive, marker for colorectal cancer. Improvement of assays lead to increased sensitivity but reduced specificity for malignancy, and loss of specificity for the colon. The problem is that CEA, like all tumour antigens, is present in normal tissue. There are in fact a large number of different CEA molecules, all of which have the domain structure of immunoglobulins and are derived from the immunoglobulin super-gene family. The CEA gene family, on chromosome 19, includes CEA, the non-specific cross-reacting antigens (NCA) and the pregnancy specific glycoproteins. The NCA family includes a number of previously identified granulocyte markers such as CD66. The original CEA antibody was polyvalent and cross-reacted with NCA, a fact which may have increased its value as a tumour marker as NCA is also present in colorectal and other cancers. As CEA extracted from tissue is not a patented epitope defined by a specific antibody, a range of monoclonal antibodies has been produced by different workers. Not surprisingly this has lead to different results and varying claims of specificity and sensitivity. A joint attempt in 1989 to clarify the situation led to the classification of existing monoclonal antibodies into five essentially non-overlapping epitope groups named Gold 1 - 5. This, and subsequent work, has shown that groups 1, 2 and 3 have the highest specificity for true CEA while most cross-reacting antibodies are in groups 4 and 5.

Plasma concentrations of CEA are increased in many malignancies. While it is used mainly for monitoring gastrointestinal tract carcinoma, particularly of the colon, CEA has also been used to monitor a range of other cancers that do not have their own 'special marker'. These include tumours of the female reproductive system, bladder and head and neck.

MUCINS

Many marker antibodies are directed at epitopes on one or more of the mucins (glycoproteins) found on cell surfaces in the gastrointestinal, respiratory and reproductive tracts and in the breast. These consist of a protein core, or apomucin, which is highly glycosylated. Seven of these have been identified in different tissues and named MUC1 to MUC7. MUC1 is the main one involved in tumour markers and is a large transmembrane molecule. In malignancy these molecules may be synthesised in increased amounts and may, because of imperfect post-translational processing, develop unique epitopes or expose normally hidden epitopes. It is possible that, while there is no tumour-specific molecule, tumour-specific epitopes may yet be identified.

Plasma concentrations of these markers are increased in a range of epithelial malignancies as well as in benign conditions. They are removed from the circulation by the liver, so liver disease may be a cause of elevated values.

The **CA 19-9** assay detects the sialylated form of the Lewis[a] blood group antigen and so is not present in the 10% or so of individuals who lack this antigen. It is used mainly for monitoring pancreatic carcinoma.

The **CA 242** assay is an example of the newer gastrointestinal tract (GIT) markers. It uses two antibodies, one against sialylated Lewis[a] and the other a different antibody called C 242. It is used in monitoring GIT cancers.

The **CA 15-3** assay uses one antibody (115 D8) to the human milk fat globule membrane and a second (DF3) to an epitope extracted from breast carcinoma. It is used mainly for monitoring breast carcinoma.

The **CA 125** assay detects an epitope, identified by the OC 125 antibody, on a mucin-like glycoprotein of MW>200kD that is present in tissues derived from the fetal coelomic epithelium. In the adult it occurs on the pleura and peritoneum, the gastro-intestinal tract and female reproductive tract, including the endometrium, as well as in many body secretions. In health, plasma CA 125 levels are usually below 35 kU/L and are higher in women younger than 49 years than in older women and in males. Elevations occur in women at the time of menstruation and may exceed this value and may be very high in early pregnancy. It is used mainly for ovarian cancer.

β_2 -MICROGLOBULIN
β_2-microglobulin (B2M) is the light chain of the class 1 major histocompatibility antigens (HCA) present on the surface of all nucleated cells. It is used in the monitoring of B cell tumours, particularly multiple myeloma.

CYTOKERATINS
Cytokeratins are intermediate filaments of the cytoskeleton. More than twenty, expressed variably in different tissues, have been described. Increased production is reflected by a rise in the level in the blood where the soluble fragments can be measured. Several assays have been used.

Examples of the cytokeratins include:

- CYFRA 21, which detects cytokeratin 19 (p. 60);
- tissue polypeptide antigen (TPA);
- tissue polypeptide specific antigen (TPS).

Tissue polypeptide antigen is related to breakdown products of cytokeratins 8, 18 and 19 which are most abundant in malignant tissue. These are synthesised and released when cells grow and divide. Plasma levels reflect tumour proliferative activity, not tumour mass, in a wide range of tumours and many non-malignant disorders. They have been used in conjunction with other markers, or alone if there is no other suitable marker. Rising concentrations may precede symptoms of recurrence by months but are not specific as elevations also occur in infections and liver disease. TPA has a half-life of 1 - 3 days. The tissue polypeptide specific antigen (TPS) assay uses a monoclonal antibody to one of the epitopes detected in TPA assays.

SECRETION PRODUCTS AND ENZYMES

As indicated in Chapter 5, many of the secretions of malignant cells are of clinical importance. As tumour markers, they have a relatively greater specificity for cell type of origin than do the structural markers.

Alphafetoprotein (AFP), a heterogenous glycoprotein of molecular weight approximately 70 kD, was identified as a major protein in fetal serum in 1956 and, in 1973, was found in the serum of patients with hepatocellular carcinoma. In the embryo it is synthesised and secreted initially by the yolk sac and, later by the fetal gastrointestinal tract and liver. It is a major plasma protein in the fetus and may function like albumin, with which it has about 30% structural homology. The very high plasma concentrations in the fetus (1-3 g/L) result in diffusion into the amniotic fluid and maternal plasma where concentrations rise during pregnancy. Increased passage through exposed vascular beds, as occurs in spina bifida, causes the higher maternal plasma AFP concentrations that form the basis of the screening test for neural tube defects. At birth, plasma concentrations are still many thousand times higher than in the adult but reach adult levels of <10 $\mu g/L$ at about the age of 1 - 2 years. High concentrations may persist in some families as an autosomal dominant inherited condition. It is of value in patients with hepatocellular carcinoma and germ cell tumours.

Human chorionic gonadotropin (hCG) is a glycoprotein hormone produced by trophoblastic tissue. This is found in the placenta in normal pregnancy, in choriocarcinoma and in trophoblastic (i.e. extraembryonal) elements in germ cell tumours. Small amounts are also produced by the anterior pituitary gland. HCG consists of two subunits, the α-subunit being identical to the α-subunit of the other pituitary glycoprotein hormones (FSH, LH, TSH). The β-subunit is similar to that of LH but is larger, and can be specifically measured by monoclonal antibodies. Several forms of HCG may be present in plasma and urine: the intact molecule, free α- and β-subunits and the inactive breakdown products, 'nicked' HCG and the β-core fragment. Different assay systems react differently with these different forms so it is important to select the most suitable one and to use the same method to monitor a patient. Trophoblastic tumours produce more free β-HCG than does benign trophoblast and the assay chosen to monitor such tumours should measure both the free β-subunit and the intact molecule. HCG secretion may occur in a range of other tumours of the reproductive system, lung and gastrointestinal tract but the concentrations reached in these are generally not suitable for use as a marker. It is highest and most useful in patients with germ cell tumours.

Other secretion products are discussed in relation to the situations in which they are used. They include:

- prostate-specific antigen   (p. 66)
- des-gamma-carboxy prothrombin   (p. 57)
- neuronspecific enolase   (p. 60)
- placental-like alkaline phosphatase   (p. 65)
- thyroglobulin   (p. 70)
- paraproteins and Bence Jones protein   (p. 72)
- catecholamines   (p. 73)
- chromogranins   (p. 75).

NONSPECIFIC MARKERS OF CELL TURNOVER

There are several markers which reflect cell turnover or proliferation. Most are non-specific but have been used, alone or in conjunction with other tumour markers, for monitoring tumours which do not have more specific markers.

NEOPTERIN

Neopterin is a breakdown product of pteridine metabolism and reflects active macrophages. This in turn reflects interferon-γ production from activated T-lymphocytes. Raised concentrations in blood or urine are found in any condition associated with increased immunological activity. Normally this is short-lived but high concentrations persist in immune deficient states, such as HIV-I infection and malignancy. This apparently contradictory finding may relate to impaired disposal of neopterin. It is therefore a non-specific indicator of the impaired immunity of advanced malignancy and has been used as a prognostic indicator in myeloma and other haematological malignancies.

THYMIDINE KINASE

Thymidine kinase is a key enzyme in the salvage pathway of DNA synthesis. Its production and plasma concentrations relate to cell proliferative activity and it has been used in the monitoring of myeloma and other haematological malignancies.

TUMOUR-ASSOCIATED TRYPSIN INHIBITOR (TATI)

This peptide, synthesised in the gastro-intestinal tract mucosa as well as in several tumours, behaves as an acute phase reactant. It has been used for tumours such as renal and gastric carcinoma but is non-specific.

INTERPRETATION OF TUMOUR MARKERS

The ideal tumour marker would:

- be detectable only when malignancy is present;

- be specific for the types and site of the malignancy;

- correlate with the amount of malignant tissue present (tumour burden);

- respond rapidly to change in tumour size.

Let it be said at the outset that, at present, there is no marker that fulfils all these criteria.

Many currently used markers have been produced by raising monoclonal antibodies to extracts of tumour tissue to detect something not present in normal tissue. In many cases, the epitope identified is defined only by the antibody used and the nature of the 'marker' molecule on which it occurs is not known, at least at first. These antibodies may be used to detect the markers in histological preparations of a tumour where they provide additional information about the nature of the tumour. In this situation however, the diagnosis of malignancy has already been established by histological criteria. When the antibody is adapted to measuring the marker in blood or other body fluids this is not the case and, as all markers may be produced by normal tissue, the distinction between benign and malignant must be made on quantitative grounds. There are however, many causes of increased 'tumour marker' concentrations other than malignancy (Figure 3.1).

Factors influencing plasma tumour marker concentrations

- production

- vascularity

- excretion

- disposal

Figure 3.1   Factors influencing plasma tumour marker concentrations

If a particular marker is produced by a particular tissue, plasma concentrations may increase if:

- There is increased production. This may be due to benign or malignant cell proliferation, or to increased expression of the marker by the malignant cell.

- Increased amounts of the marker enter the bloodstream. Increased vascularity due, for example to inflammation, enhances the passage of marker into the blood and leads to higher plasma concentrations. In malignancy, disruption of normal cell relationships and tissue boundaries permits easier access to the circulation.

- There is a decrease in the rate of disposal of the marker. If the marker is something that is normally secreted, such as PSA is into the seminal fluid, the distorted architecture of tumour growth may disturb the normal anatomical relationship between cells and secretory passages and result in diversion of the marker into the blood stream. As many markers are removed from the circulation by the liver, liver disease may result in reduced clearance and higher plasma concentrations.

MARKERS FOR THE DETECTION OF MALIGNANCY

The detection and diagnosis of cancer by a blood test is an emotive and ethically charged issue and as a group, the tumour marker tests are probably one of the most publicised diagnostic procedures. Particular markers are linked to particular tumours and may be requested by doctors unaware of their limitations both in diagnosing the presence of a cancer, and defining its nature. In this area misuse and misinterpretation can have disastrous consequences. The role in diagnosis – both in screening asymptomatic patients and investigating those with symptoms, is particularly misunderstood.

The rationale of any screening test is to detect a subgroup of the population that is more likely to have a particular disease and in which further diagnostic tests are justified. This is in order to detect disease at a preclinical stage and presupposes that such early detection and treatment will benefit the patient. Unfortunately this is not necessarily the case and it has become clear that the natural history of some tumours is poorly understood. Furthermore, the use of plasma tumour markers for screening is limited by:

- the non-specificity of most markers for malignancy;

- the low prevalence of any particular cancer at a given point;

- the fact that small, and potentially treatable, tumours may not give rise to elevated values.

When used in selected populations or patient groups under defined conditions, markers may be of greater diagnostic value but it is essential to recognise their limitations.

In assessing any marker proposed for diagnostic purposes one needs to know the sensitivity and specificity of the test and the prevalence of the cancer in the relevant population (see Appendix for details).

Sensitivity, or the ability to detect the disease when present, is defined by the percentage of those with the disease in whom a positive result is obtained.

Specificity, or the ability to exclude the disease when absent, is defined by the percentage of those without the disease in whom a negative result is obtained.

An ideal marker would have a sensitivity and specificity of 100%. None meet this ideal; most evaluations report sensitivity at a specificity of 95%.

Consider the use of a marker with a sensitivity of 95% and a specificity of 95%. If the test is to be used in an apparently healthy population, i.e. as a screening test, to detect a malignancy with a prevalence of 20 per 100,000 then:

- 19 of those with malignancy will be detected, 1 will not;

- 4999 of those without malignancy will have false positive results. The true positives are lost in the noise of the false positives and the test is of little value for this purpose, particularly as the diagnosis is so serious.

If however, the test is used in a population known to be at risk for the malignancy, and in which the prevalence is 10% or 10,000 in 100,000 then:

- 9500 of those with malignancy will be detected, 500 will not;

- 4500 of those without malignancy will have false positive results.

Two out of three positive results will be true positives and the test may be practical. For most tumours the situation is closer to the first example.

The classification of a result as positive or negative is based on whether it is greater or less than a defined value or cut-off point. Clearly this cut-off point determines the sensitivity and specificity and may be varied to meet the clinical requirement. If it is imperative to find as many cases of cancer as possible, the cut-off should be selected to achieve this but will inevitably lead to a loss of specificity. Similarly, if it is considered important not to subject too many people to unnecessary confirmatory tests, the cut-off should be selected for optimal specificity. This of course will reduce the sensitivity. This relationship is expressed by noting the receiver operating characteristics (ROC) of the test, and tumour marker evaluations should express results this way. ROC curves are particularly useful when comparing different markers in the same clinical setting.

It is important to realise that even if an evaluation provides all the data discussed above, it applies only to the patient categories evaluated and may not be applicable to other situations.

SUSPECTED MALIGNANCY

If a patient presents with symptoms suggestive of a particular malignancy, there are still problems in using tumour markers for diagnosis. While the *a priori* likelihood of a malignancy being present is greater i.e. the prevalence may be greater, the presence of symptoms indicates pathology that may in itself cause false positive results. In general, but by no means invariably, the higher the plasma concentration of the marker, the greater the likelihood of it being due to cancer. A firm diagnosis depends on other evidence, preferably histological, of malignancy.

Even if the concentration is so high as to make malignancy extremely likely, the non-specificity of the marker molecules for any particular tissue is such that the site may not be obvious and again other investigations are needed. A particular problem in this regard is the patient who is found to have disseminated malignancy with no obvious primary site. This is further considered on p. 75.

MARKERS FOR PROGNOSIS AND MONITORING

There is often a reasonable correlation between the plasma concentration of the marker and tumour mass and this has been used as one factor in determining prognosis and selecting appropriate therapy.

In monitoring, the extent of the fall after therapy is some indication of its success and failure to reach normal concentrations suggests residual tumour. The time to achieve normal concentrations varies widely depending on:

- the initial concentration;
- the half-life of the marker. Small molecules that are excreted, such as HCG, are cleared more rapidly than the larger molecules which are metabolised;
- the nature of the therapy. Surgical removal of a tumour results in a more rapid fall than chemotherapy or radiotherapy.

Following chemotherapy there may be a transient elevation as stored marker is released from cells. This may last for a few days (HCG) or weeks (CEA), so follow-up samples should be taken after this time. A failure of marker concentrations to fall enables alternative therapy, if available, to be instituted.

The detection of recurrence depends on demonstrating a significant rise in the plasma concentration of the marker on more than one occasion, and excluding other causes of such a rise. The level of change that is significant depends both on the analytical imprecision of the assay and any *in vivo* variation of the marker. Both may be considerable and this has lead to the rule of thumb that a doubling or halving of the concentration is significant. A progressive rise of lower magnitude is also significant. These factors will be considered for the individual markers. In monitoring treatment it is important to remember that malignant tumours consist of different cell types, not all of which may secrete the marker being measured. A change of the cellular composition after treatment may result in a fall in tumour marker concentrations, despite progression of the tumour. Plasma markers are only one element of monitoring.

THE PROBLEM OF ASSAY VARIABILITY
The interpretation of results is further complicated by analytical factors such as:

- **Non-specificity**. As mentioned above, most current markers have been identified by developing antibodies to tumour tissue and in some cases the marker is defined only by the relevant antibody used. The antibody in turn recognises an epitope on a molecule. This epitope may be variably expressed in different tumours, or variations in the basic molecule may make the epitope in malignancy more, or less, accessible to the antibody than it is in benign tissue. Furthermore, cross reaction with similar epitopes on different molecules may lead to lack of specificity, a problem that may be partly overcome by using a sandwich type assay with the two antibodies directed at separate epitopes on the marker molecule. For most markers there are several assays available. These may use different antibodies, ostensibly to the same marker molecule, but may react with different epitopes and produce discordant results. Even the same antibody, if altered by a different way of labelling, may behave differently in certain patients. Finally, standardisation is a major problem as it is often not possible to produce an appropriate pure standard of the marker molecule, even if its nature is known. The result is that most tumour marker assays should be considered as empirical tests. In following the progress of a patient, samples should be assayed by the same method to permit comparison of results. The quirks of particular assays will be considered in the following chapter where relevant.

- **Human antimouse antibodies** (HAMA) which may react with the monoclonal antibodies (of mouse origin) in the assay to produce a false signal. While most reagent kits attempt to overcome this by including mouse serum in the reagents, this may not always be enough. As more patients are treated with mouse monoclonal antibodies, for imaging or therapy, this problem may increase.

- **The hook effect.** Laboratories need also be aware of which assays may show a 'hook effect', whereby extremely high concentrations swamp the antibody used in competitive binding assay and may be read as low or normal.

- The **reproducibility** of the assay is also important in defining significant changes. For most, the CV is about 10%.

THE CLINICAL RELEVANCE OF TUMOUR MARKERS

The extensive literature on tumour markers obscures the fact that many have only limited clinical relevance. Even in the area of monitoring, their routine use must be critically evaluated.

The first question is whether or not a marker truly reflects what is happening to a tumour. In many cases it does but there are sufficient exceptions to make reliance on plasma markers alone unwise. The failure of a marker concentration to fall after chemotherapy does not always indicate that the treatment is not effective and a decision to stop or to change therapy requires additional information. Many markers may detect recurrence of a tumour before there is clinical evidence of this but, if there is no effective treatment or if treatment given at this early stage is no more successful than if given when symptoms develop, there seems little point in early detection. Some clinicians may discuss marker results with the patient but while a normal value is reassuring, an increase will provoke extreme anxiety and probably lead to further investigations. As stressed above, a normal result does not exclude recurrence nor does a rising value indicate it. The understandable desire of the clinician to know what is happening may be able to be satisfied by cheaper tests or by clinical observation.

This argument may change as treatment options improve and it is for this reason that ongoing evaluation of the behaviour of markers in different malignancies is necessary. Their use however, in individual patients should be tempered by the question - will this result change anything?

THE RECEIVER OPERATING CHARACTERISTIC (ROC) CURVE

ROC curves (Figure 3.2) are a graphic way of showing how a test performs in terms of sensitivity and specificity. If a marker is measured in a defined population of a known number of persons with and without the disease in question, the sensitivity and specificity can be calculated for a range of cut-off points. These can then be plotted and produce a graph that will define the specificity for any desired sensitivity and vice versa. An ROC curve is particularly useful for comparing two tests under the same conditions but, like all evaluations, is applicable only to populations similar to the one tested.

For further information see: Metz C E. Basic principles of ROC analysis. *Sem Nucl Med* 1978; VIII: 283-298.

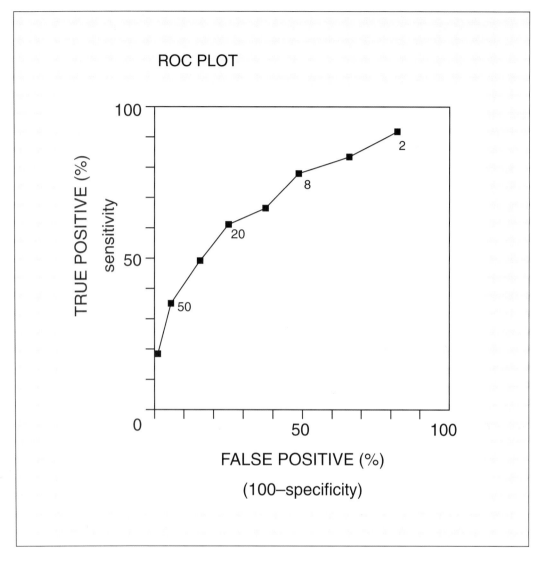

Figure 3.2   In this hypothetical example, a new tumour marker has been measured
             in a population, some of whom have the tumour it is supposed to detect.
             The percentages of true positives (sensitivity) and false positives (100 -
             specificity) have been calculated for a range of cut-off points and
             plotted. From this the sensitivity and specificity at any cut-off point can
             be read. The closer the curve is to the upper left corner, the better the test
             for the purpose

FURTHER READING
Relevant articles are listed after Chapter 4

Chapter 4

Tumours and Tumour Markers – Applications

In the preceding chapter it was stressed that the use of tumour markers was empirical. Different tumour types grow and spread differently and vary in their susceptibility to available therapy. It should not be assumed that a particular marker will behave in the same way, or that a particular level has the same significance, in different tumour types. This chapter will outline some of the current uses.

GASTROINTESTINAL TRACT MALIGNANCY

STOMACH CANCER

Biochemical tests have no role in the diagnosis and are of no practical value in the monitoring of gastric carcinoma. CEA is elevated in about half the cases but reflects tumour burden poorly and changes do not influence therapy.

CANCER OF THE COLON AND RECTUM

Cancer of the colon or rectum is one of the commonest malignancies in developed countries. Most, if not all, develop from adenomatous polyps over a period of up to ten years (p. 15) but only about 5% of polyps become malignant. If detected while still confined to the bowel wall, survival after surgery is good. People with a family history of colon cancer, familial polyposis and those with bowel disease, particularly ulcerative colitis and to a lesser extent Crohn's disease are at high risk. Patients may present with symptoms referable to the bowel, with anaemia due to blood loss, or with evidence of spread. Metastasis is most commonly to the liver.

DIAGNOSIS
Tumour markers have no place in the early diagnosis of colorectal cancer.

The detection of blood in faeces as a pointer to possible gastrointestinal malignancy was discussed on p. 29. Colorectal cancers usually bleed, as do some polyps, and occult blood testing is an important step in diagnosis as well as in follow-up after surgery. The aim of testing for faecal blood is to detect early cancer and bleeding adenomatous polyps in order to identify patients for further investigation by, for example, colonoscopy. Specific assays for human haemoglobin are inherently more specific for colorectal bleeding than the chemical tests and sensitivity in patients with cancer ranges from 80 - 97%. To avoid false negative results, samples should be fresh and properly collected and at least three specimens should be tested.

Several large studies using the guaiac test have investigated screening of populations over the age of 45 by faecal occult blood testing every two years. These have shown a lowering of mortality from colorectal cancer of about 15%, but the optimal methods and test intervals are yet to be established.

While several of the structural markers may be raised in patients with colorectal cancer, the most useful one is CEA. CA19-9 has been used but offers no more than does CEA. In the normal large bowel CEA is present on the apical surface of the mucosal cell (Figure 4.1) where it increases in concentration as the cell travels up the gland crypt to be sloughed off into the faeces. About 70 mg a day of CEA is excreted in this way, with only a small amount entering the blood. In colorectal cancer, not only is the expression of CEA increased, but the disturbance of normal architecture diverts it from this route of excretion into the blood, adding to its sensitivity as a tumour marker.

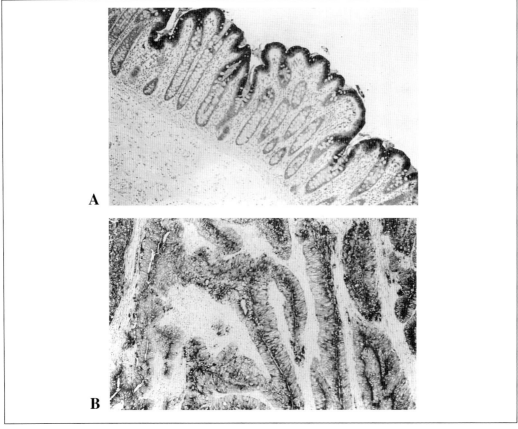

Figure 4.1   These two photomicrographs of tissue, treated with peroxidase-linked CEA antibody, show the distribution of CEA (darker areas) in normal colon and in colon cancer. In the normal tissue (A) the CEA appears in the cells lining the surface from where they slough off into the lumen. In the malignant tissue (B) this clearly cannot happen and the CEA enters the blood

Most healthy people have plasma CEA concentrations of less than 2.5 μg/L, and virtually all have concentrations less than 5 μg/L. Higher concentrations may be found in smokers.

Plasma concentrations are raised in colorectal and other gastrointestinal tract malignancies as well as in cancer of the breast, lung and other tissues. Non-malignant causes include inflammatory bowel disease and chronic liver disease. The blood concentrations in non-malignant conditions are usually less than 10 μg/L. The precise concentration and prevalence of raised values in non-gastrointestinal tract cancers depend on the assay as many of the tumours express NCA (p. 41) as well, or only NCA.

The proportion of patients with colorectal cancer that have plasma CEA concentrations of >5 μg/L ranges from less than 10% in patients with localised lesions to about 70% in those with disseminated disease. It is therefore neither sensitive nor specific enough for screening and cannot be recommended for that purpose. As a diagnostic test in symptomatic patients its value depends on the clinical situation but in general concentrations of greater than 50 μg/L are suggestive of malignancy.

PROGNOSIS AND MONITORING

Patients with plasma CEA concentrations greater than 5 μg/L before surgery have a significantly worse prognosis than those with values below this. This probably reflects a larger tumour mass or the presence of unsuspected liver metastases. It has been shown experimentally that high CEA-producing cell lines have greater metastatic capability.

The half-life of CEA is about three days. After successful surgery plasma concentrations usually return to normal after 4 to 6 weeks but may take longer. Failure to do so suggests residual tumour. Follow up samples to detect recurrence, usually taken at three monthly intervals, are indicated if detection would influence management (Figure 4.2). For example, hepatic secondaries may be surgically removed with a cure rate of about 20%. Several studies have shown increasing plasma CEA concentrations 3 to 6 months before clinical signs of recurrence. Defining an increase has problems as short-term rises from other causes may occur, but a rise or fall of more than 25% is widely considered as being significant. A smaller but progressive and sustained rise over several samples is probably significant. Random intrapatient variation is about 6%, less than the precision of most assays.

CEA has been measured in other fluids such as pleural and peritoneal effusions and in cyst fluids. Concentrations in such fluids are often higher than those in plasma, even in the absence of malignancy. In general, a high concentration favours malignancy but has to be interpreted in the full clinical setting.

Labelled CEA antibodies have been used to aid *in vivo* detection of tumour. It is in this area that careful selection of the antibody is important to increase specificity for malignant tissue.

The use of CEA in guiding treatment

This 64 year old man was diagnosed with colon carcinoma and the tumour was removed. At operation he was noted to have metastases in the liver so, after a short recovery period, chemotherapy was begun. The drug used was 5-fluorouracil (5FU) and the dosage and method of administration was guided by plasma CEA concentrations.

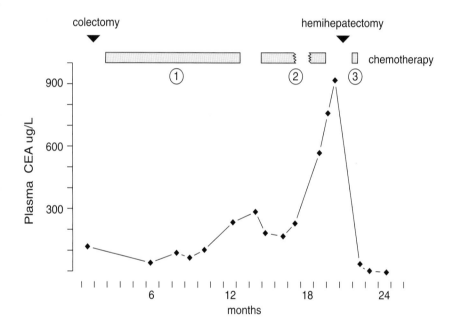

① 5FU given in **cycles.**

② 5FU given by **continuous intravenous infusion**. When this failed, the right half of the liver, which contained most of the secondary tumour, was removed and a cannula was put into the hepatic artery.

③ 5FU by **intrahepatic arterial infusion.**

Figure 4.2   The use of CEA in guiding treatment

PANCREATIC CANCER

Carcinoma of the pancreas is much less common than colorectal cancer. Early clinical symptoms are minimal and the tumour is usually only diagnosed at a late stage. Tumours in the head of the pancreas usually present when they obstruct the common bile duct that runs through this part of the organ and produce cholestatic (obstructive) jaundice. Tumours elsewhere in the pancreas are usually silent until liver secondaries develop. Rarely, obstruction of the pancreatic duct causes pancreatitis and even more rarely, destruction of much of the organ may produce, or aggravate, diabetes mellitus as the islet cells are destroyed.

CEA has been used in assessment and monitoring as has the mucin marker CA19-9. At the time of diagnosis of advanced tumours, CA 19-9 is elevated in about 80% of patients. At that sensitivity the specificity, when compared against benign pancreatic disease, is only about 60%. A relevant problem is the high concentrations found with extrahepatic biliary obstruction, regardless of cause, and in chronic liver disease. Its use in monitoring is limited by lack of effective treatment. Concentrations are often elevated in other cancers of the gastrointestinal tract but CA 19-9 does not offer significantly more than CEA in this area.

Thus measurement of CA 19-9 offers no benefit to patients with pancreatic cancer.

The performance of CA 242 is similar to that of CA 19-9 in the diagnosis of pancreatic cancer. It has a sensitivity of 70 - 80% but has higher specificity (91%). Of note is that it is elevated in 60% of patients in whom surgical treatment is potentially curative. It seems to be less affected by extrahepatic obstruction than is CA 19-9.

HEPATOCELLULAR CARCINOMA

Primary liver cancer (hepatocellular carcinoma) is a common tumour in Africa and Asia where it is associated with chronic liver disease, particularly chronic hepatitis B and C, and occurs in young people (<30 years). In other parts of the world the tumour develops usually at a later age, is commoner in males, and usually develops in patients with cirrhosis due to hepatitis B or C, or in patients with hereditary haemochromatosis. Hepatocellular carcinoma grows rapidly and has a very poor prognosis though survival may be prolonged by treatment if the lesion is small at diagnosis and is resectable. The main tumour marker used is alphafetoprotein (AFP).

Plasma AFP is elevated in hepatocellular carcinoma and hepatoblastoma as well as germ cell and yolk sac tumours. Less commonly elevations are seen with gastric, pancreatic and gall bladder cancer.

There are several non-malignant causes of raised values, particularly conditions associated with hepatic necrosis and regeneration (viral and other forms of hepatitis) as well as cirrhosis and primary biliary cirrhosis. Extrahepatic biliary obstruction may also elevate concentrations and rare causes are hereditary tyrosinaemia and hereditary persistence of high concentrations.

It is interesting that regeneration of the liver after partial hepatectomy does not usually result in an AFP rise. This may be because it involves proliferation of more mature cells.

AFP IN HEPATIC MALIGNANCY

Plasma AFP is elevated in the majority of patients with hepatocellular carcinoma but the reported sensitivity varies widely from country to country. However, up to 10% of tumours do not produce this marker.

Plasma AFP measurement, together with ultrasound examination, has been used to detect the development of hepatocellular carcinoma in high risk patient groups, and in the differential diagnosis of a liver mass. This use in high risk groups is complicated by the raised values that occur in the underlying conditions such as cirrhosis and chronic hepatitis, particularly during periods of disease activity. In most of these, plasma AFP values remain less than 200 μg/L but they exceed that in only 50 - 60% of patients with hepatocellular carcinoma. A value of 500 μg/L or more is virtually diagnostic of malignancy. In patients with hepatocellular carcinoma the plasma AFP concentration correlates with the size of the tumour and the degree of differentiation, and has some prognostic significance. Patients with values greater than 1000 μg/L rarely survive more than 6 months.

There have been several attempts to improve the distinction between benign and malignant causes of raised values, based on the degree of glycosylation of AFP. It has been shown that the forms found in hepatocellular carcinoma and germ cell tumours may be distinguished by lectin affinity chromatography. Other separation techniques, including isoelectric focusing, have shown that patterns of AFP forms may distinguish between benign and malignant causes. These tests are not suitable for large scale use but may help in evaluating moderate AFP elevation in a particular case.

DES-GAMMA-CARBOXY PROTHROMBIN

This is another marker for hepatocellular carcinoma. Prothrombin is a vitamin K-dependent coagulation factor that is synthesised in the liver. In patients given the anticoagulant warfarin, an abnormal and inactive form appears in the blood while normal, active prothrombin concentrations fall. The abnormal form is deficient in carboxyglutamic acid and has been variously called des-gamma-carboxy prothrombin (DCP) or 'prothrombin induced by vitamin K absence or antagonist-II' (PIVKA-II). Hepatocellular carcinoma cells synthesise DCP despite adequate vitamin K and normal concentrations of native prothrombin, and this has been evaluated as a tumour marker with some success. Raised concentrations are found in just over half of the patients with hepatocellular carcinoma and correlate with tumour size. There is no direct correlation with AFP concentrations, and in monitoring, changes in the two markers may not always coincide. The greatest value seems to be the much better distinction between carcinoma and chronic liver disease such as cirrhosis. With increasing experience and standardisation of assays DCP may become a useful assay in screening patients at risk.

BREAST CANCER

Carcinoma of the breast is the commonest malignancy in women and, if detected early, is curable. Plasma tumour markers have no role in such detection which relies on self-screening and mammography. Markers in plasma and in the carcinomatous tissue itself are some help in prognosis and monitoring. Treatment is by surgical removal with chemotherapy for metastatic disease.

CEA (or possibly NCA) is elevated in less than a quarter of patients with early disease and in up to three quarters of those with advanced carcinoma, particularly those with liver and bone metastases. In some cases it reflects the response to therapy and is useful in monitoring.

CA 15-3 is the marker of greatest value. The assay detects one of the mucins and so suffers from all the non-specificity of that group, with elevations occurring in benign and malignant disease of the lung, gastrointestinal and reproductive systems as well as with liver disease. The sensitivity in early stages of breast cancer ranges from 0 - 36% and, in advanced disease up to 100%, with specificity against benign breast disease of 85 - 100%, depending on the cut-off value selected. The concentration reflects tumour burden and a level of greater than five times the cut-off value suggests metastatic disease.

Patients in whom CA 15-3 returns to normal (<30kU/L) after treatment have a better prognosis than those in whom it does not. In monitoring, the lead time between a rise in plasma concentrations and clinical recurrence may be up to several months. A rise of greater than 25% is considered a significant change. In monitoring therapy of metastatic disease, decreasing marker concentrations indicate response but steady or rising values do not exclude it.

A number of related markers have been evaluated. These include CA 549, CA M26, CA M29 and MCA (mucin-like carcinoma-associated antigen). None is clearly superior to the better evaluated CA 15-3. The interested reader is referred to the reading list at the end of the chapter.

A different type of marker that has been used in following breast cancer is the tissue polypeptide antigen (see p. 42). It reflects proliferation rather than tumour mass and is claimed to be a more sensitive indicator of progression.

TISSUE MARKERS

Oestrogens, from the ovary or converted from adrenal steroids by enzymes (aromatases) in the tumour, have long been known to promote the growth of breast cancers. Antioestrogens such as tamoxifen, and aromatase inhibitors such as aminoglutethimide are used in treatment. The concentration of oestrogen and progesterone receptors in the tumour tissue correlates well with the likelihood that the tumour will respond to hormone therapy and is a good prognostic marker. Some receptor-negative patients however may respond to hormonal manipulation. Receptors are usually measured by radio-ligand binding. Immunocytochemical assays are available but less well evaluated.

Other changes have been noted but, at present, do not influence management. Over-expression of the p53 tumour-suppressor gene is a negative prognostic indicator and correlates with the absence of oestrogen receptor activity. Amplification of the proto-oncogene HER-2/neu (c-erbB-2), and over-expression of the protein product are also poor prognostic indicators, as is the oestrogen-induced glycoprotein, cathepsin D. This has growth-promoting activity and high tumour concentrations are associated with a poorer prognosis.

LUNG CANCER

Primary lung cancer is one of the main causes of cancer deaths in developed countries. The major types are shown in Figure 4.3

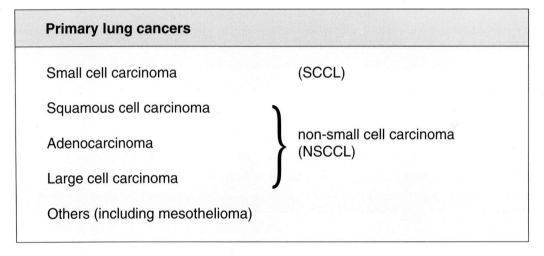

Primary lung cancers

Small cell carcinoma (SCCL)

Squamous cell carcinoma

Adenocarcinoma   non-small cell carcinoma (NSCCL)

Large cell carcinoma

Others (including mesothelioma)

Figure 4.3   Primary lung cancers

Unless detected incidentally on chest Xray, most lung cancers present at a late stage with local symptoms or distant metastases.

SMALL CELL CANCER OF THE LUNG

This neuroendocrine tumour accounts for 20 - 25% of lung cancers. It spreads early and is rarely amenable to surgical removal but often responds to chemotherapy. About half may secrete any of a number of peptide hormones or precursors such as adrenocorticotropic hormone (ACTH), arginine vasopressin (AVP) or antidiuretic hormone (ADH), neurophysin and bombesin. With the exception of ACTH, assays for these are not generally available so they are not particularly useful as tumour markers.

Assays of ACTH can be useful but:

- do not distinguish between tumour-derived and native ACTH;

- the tumour may secrete precursors.

The enzyme neuronspecific enolase (NSE) is produced by neuroendocrine tumours and plasma concentrations are raised above 12.5 μg/L in 50 - 60% of patients with SCCL confined to the lung and 86 - 90% of those with more advanced disease. At this cut-off, up to 45% of NSCCL may be positive but concentrations in SCCL tend to be higher. It may also be mildly elevated in patients with benign lung diseases. NSE is of some prognostic value in that patients with levels >25 μg/L on diagnosis have a shorter survival than those with levels <25 μg/L. Plasma NSE concentrations fall to <8 μg/L with successful chemotherapy.

Another enzyme, creatine kinase BB may also be elevated in SCCL but offers no advantage over NSE. It is elevated in less than 5% of patients with localised disease.

NON-SMALL CELL CARCINOMA OF THE LUNG
These tumours usually present with local symptoms or with evidence of distant spread. Hypercalcaemia is a recognised presenting feature (p. 83). This group differs from SCCL in that therapy is mainly by surgical resection, although the patients may respond well to chemotherapy and radiation therapy.

CEA is elevated in about a third of cases and is of some prognostic value in that the higher the concentration, the greater the tumour burden and the worse the prognosis.

An assay that is being increasingly promoted is CYFRA 21-1 (CYtokeratin FRAgments) using antibodies 21 and 1. It detects cytokeratin 19 which is abundant in NSCCL. At a specificity of 95% against benign lung disease (a level of 3.3 μg/L) the overall sensitivity for NSCCL is 51% (62% for squamous cell carcinoma). It is elevated in about 20% of SCCL. Other causes, or contributing factors to elevated concentrations, are renal failure and liver disease. In malignancy values correlate with tumour burden and contribute to staging of the disease. In monitoring, rises in CYFRA 21-1 have preceded clinical recurrence by 2 - 6 months. CYFRA 21-1 is a non-specific marker and elevated values have been noted in malignancy of the gastrointestinal tract, and of the genitourinary tract including the prostate.

Squamous cell carcinoma antigen (SCCA), originally called TA-4, was isolated from a squamous cell carcinoma of the cervix. Plasma concentrations are raised in a range of squamous carcinomas of different organs. The sensitivity in SCCL is about 50%, slightly less than that of CYFRA 21-1.

OVARIAN CANCER

Cancer of the ovary develops in about one percent of women, usually over the age of 50. While several tumour markers are of value in management, none are sensitive or specific enough for screening.

The commonest types (>80%) arise from the ovarian epithelium and are hormonally inactive. The prevalence of this type in the post-menopausal age group is about 30/100000 and most patients present with advanced disease. Spread is most commonly through the peritoneal cavity and regional lymph nodes. Tumours arising from the ovarian stroma, comprising about 5% of all tumours, may produce either oestrogens or androgens which may result in uterine bleeding or virilisation. Germ cell tumours occur in girls and young women and are rare after the age of 30.

EPITHELIAL TUMOURS

The plasma assay of most value is CA 125. Concentrations are increased in epithelial ovarian cancer but also in a range of malignancies of the gastrointestinal tract, lung and breast. CA 125 is also elevated in several benign gynaecological conditions such as endometriosis where, in diagnosed disease, the CA 125 value correlates with the extent of the disease and responds to therapy-induced changes.

Epithelial ovarian tumours	Relative frequencies (%)
Serous adenocarcinoma	50-60
Mucinous adenocarcinoma	15
Rarer forms are endometrioid, clear cell and undifferentiated adenocarcinoma	25-35

Figure 4.4   Epithelial ovarian tumours

Other causes include uterine fibroids, benign ovarian tumours, pelvic inflammatory disease and chronic liver disease, especially with ascites. Ascites, of any cause, is a particularly important confounding factor. Plasma CA 125 values may be several hundred units, overlapping the range characteristic of extensive malignancy. The test is of no value in checking for undiagnosed ovarian cancer as a cause of ascites.

CA 125 IN OVARIAN CANCER

The CA 125 antigen is present in serous adenocarcinoma of the ovary but not in mucinous tumours. In normal women, plasma concentrations are <35 kU/L and are elevated in 80 - 85% of cases of serous adenocarcinoma on diagnosis, ranging from 50% of cases where the tumour is confined to the ovary, to >90% of those in which dissemination has occurred. Concentrations tend to be higher in moderately or poorly differentiated tumours than in highly differentiated ones. Moderate elevations occur in some cases of mucinous carcinoma, possibly due to peritoneal involvement. The limited diagnostic role of CA 125 is shown by data in the reference cited. For example, in patients with pelvic masses, a CA 125 concentration greater than 30 kU/L had a sensitivity of 81%, specificity of 75% and a positive predictive value of only 58%.

PROGNOSIS AND MONITORING

Some, but not all, studies have shown that the pre-operative CA 125 concentration is of some prognostic significance in that the survival of patients with a value <65 kU/L is greater than those with concentrations above this. The rate of fall after surgical removal and chemotherapy is also significant. Those with a half-life of CA 125 of less than 20 days tend to have a longer period before recurrence than those with a half-life of more than 20 days. In monitoring, a rise of plasma CA 125 (a doubling outside the reference range) indicates residual disease but a normal value does not exclude small-volume residual disease. It is thought that a tumour larger than 2 cm is needed to elevate plasma concentrations. There is no proven benefit in treating in the absence of clinical symptoms.

CA 125 and ovarian carcinoma

This 62 year old woman had a serous adenocarcinoma of the ovary removed. Her plasma CA 125 in the following year remained within the 'reference range' (<35 kU/L) but thereafter began to rise.

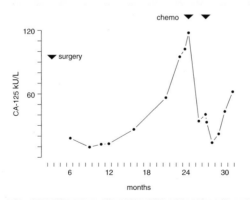

She remained symptom-free for another year before developing abdominal pain and mild ascites. Chemotherapy was then given.

These results illustrate the lead time provided by tumour markers. The clinical utility, other than keeping the doctor informed and making the patient anxious, is debatable.

Figure 4.5   CA 125 and ovarian carcinoma

CA 125 has been measured in benign cyst fluid and may be extremely high. It is also present in cervical mucus and amniotic fluid.

OTHER MARKERS

CEA and a number of mucin markers such as CA 19-9 have been used to monitor mucinous carcinoma. One that is of value in ovarian cancer is the cancer-associated serum antigen (CASA), an assay which uses two monoclonal antibodies to epitopes on the MUC1 mucin. This is present in low concentrations in healthy women, concentrations increase with age and are higher in smokers and during pregnancy. It detects a greater proportion of mucinous carcinomas than does CA 125 and it has been used to complement CA 125 in monitoring mucinous ovarian cancer, as well as in non-small cell lung cancer.

STROMAL TUMOURS

Stromal ovarian tumours include:

- Granulosa/theca cell tumours;

- Sertoli/Leydig cell tumours.

The inhibins and activins are glycoprotein hormones produced by granulosa cells of the developing ovarian follicle under the control of gonadotropins; in turn they control the secretion of FSH by feedback. Concentrations fluctuate during the menstrual cycle and rise in pregnancy. Plasma concentrations of inhibin are elevated in patients with granulosa cell tumours, over 80% of those with mucinous cystadenocarcinoma and in about 20% of those with other ovarian tumours. Unfortunately they can also be elevated in benign ovarian pathology. The relative merits of the different forms of inhibins and their role in monitoring ovarian cancer is currently under investigation. If the assay is not available, the pituitary hormones FSH and LH may be used to monitor stromal cell tumours after both ovaries have been removed. A fall from the resulting high values indicates suppression by active hormone secretion by recurrent tumour.

GERM CELL TUMOURS

This small group of tumours, less than 1% of ovarian malignancies and occurring predominantly in women less than 30 years old, develop from the primordial germ cell. Chemotherapy is successful in the majority of cases, even those presenting with extensive metastatic disease.

The germ cell may differentiate along one of two pathways, one the pathway to yolk sac or trophoblast (extraembryonal) and the other along the pathway to the embryo (embryonal). Tumours differ in marker expression depending on the differentiation of the cell of origin. Classifications vary and mixed tumours occur.

Germ cell tumours and marker expression			
	Tumour	**AFP**	**HCG**
Undifferentiated	Embryonal carcinoma	+	+
	Dysgerminoma	–	–
Extraembryonal	Endodermal sinus (yolk sac)	+	–
	Choriocarcinoma	–	+
Embryonal	Teratoma	–	–

Figure 4.6   Germ cell tumours and marker expression

Plasma HCG concentrations are raised in up to 60% of patients with germ cell tumours and the β-core fragment may appear in the urine in a similar range of tumours and has also been used as a marker for gynaecological malignancies of ovary, endometrium and cervix. It has also been used in lung and pancreatic cancers.

Alphafetoprotein (AFP) concentrations are raised in about 70% of patients with tumours derived from, or containing, yolk sac elements. Both HCG and AFP concentrations may be elevated.

Plasma lactate dehydrogenase (LD) activity may be high in patients with dysgerminoma and may be used as a marker.

PROGNOSIS AND MONITORING
In ovarian germ cell tumours the initial marker concentration does not have prognostic significance but monitoring of plasma concentrations during chemotherapy is a vital part of assessing response. HCG has a half-life of about three days, βHCG of 30 hours and AFP of 4 - 6 days. There is often a rise in marker concentrations, lasting a week or so, on beginning chemotherapy.

Another important role of the markers is in detecting recurrence. It is recommended that both should be measured, even if the original tumour did not produce markers, as the tumour composition may change. As small increases may be significant it is important to exclude other causes such as pregnancy (HCG) or chemotherapy-induced liver damage (AFP).

TESTICULAR TUMOURS
Cancer of the testis is found usually after the patient notices a lump in the testis or, in some cases, only where distant spread has occurred. 95% of testicular tumours are germ

cell tumours with presumed derivation analogous to that of the ovarian germ cell tumours. For clinical purposes however, they are divided into two groups:

- Seminoma, which accounts for about half of testicular tumours. It is treated initially by removal of the primary tumour by orchidectomy and radiotherapy, to which it is extremely sensitive.

- Non-seminomatous tumours including choriocarcinoma, embryonal carcinoma and yolk sac tumours, which are treated initially by primary resection. Adjuvant chemotherapy (p. 102) is often also given.

Recurrences of either may be treated by chemotherapy.

The non-seminomatous group, like the germ cell tumours of the ovary, may develop along the yolk sac or trophoblastic pathway and so produce AFP and/or HCG. About 60% do so. While of value in determining tumour type, prognosis and therapy, markers are essential for monitoring, with failure of either marker to return to normal after therapy indicating residual tumour. Subsequent elevations indicate recurrence providing other causes, such as chemotherapy-induced liver damage for AFP, can be excluded. Unlike most other tumours, chemotherapy is often given on marker evidence without waiting for clinical symptoms.

While about 10% of seminomas produce HCG, elevated AFP concentrations indicate that elements of germ cell tumour are present. This will change the treatment approach. They may however, produce placental-like alkaline phosphatase (PLAP) or germ cell ALP. Plasma concentrations are raised in just under half the cases at presentation and about three quarters of those with metastatic disease. Changes correspond to tumour regression or progression. Plasma LD too is raised in many cases and, while non-specific, is useful in monitoring. The LD, like that in some ovarian cancers, is predominantly LD1 and LD2.

HCG and AFP may be measured in cerebrospinal fluid to detect involvement of the central nervous system. A CSF:plasma ratio of greater than 1:60 suggests such involvement but a normal ratio does not exclude it.

EXTRAGONADAL GERM CELL TUMOURS
About 5% of germ cell tumours arise from sites other than the testis. The commonest sites are along the midline in the abdomen (retroperitoneum) or chest (mediastinum). This may reflect abnormal migration of germ cells in the embryo though a few cases may be secondary to an unrecognised testicular tumour. Most such tumours are teratomas that do not produce HCG or AFP but in others these markers may be present. Management is by chemotherapy but the prognosis is generally poor.

PROSTATE CANCER

Adenocarcinoma of the prostate is the commonest cancer in men. Early autopsy studies indicated that about 30% of men over the age of 50 have it and the incidence increases with age. Incidental findings at transurethral resection of the prostate (TURP) shows that 40 - 50% of men at the age of 80 have cancer as do 10% of all men in their 50s. However, the tumour is generally slow growing and only a fifth to a third are likely to present clinically during their lifetime. In others more aggressive growth may occur. The significance of these cancers discovered at autopsy or surgery is unclear and is one of the problems confounding early detection, which is assumed to provide a reasonable chance of cure.

Until recently the only blood test capable of detecting prostate cancer was plasma prostatic acid phosphatase. This has a low sensitivity for localised disease and raised concentrations usually indicate extension beyond the prostate. The test has been replaced by measurement of prostate specific antigen.

PROSTATE SPECIFIC ANTIGEN

Prostate specific antigen (PSA) is a serine protease that is a normal and necessary component of seminal fluid where it dissolves the seminal coagulum. It is produced by secretory cells of the acini and ducts of the prostate and other cells that express the nuclear androgen receptor; PSA production is dependent on the presence of androgens, as indeed is the growth of the prostate. Similar cells are present in periurethral glands of both sexes and male perianal glands. Tissue PSA concentrations are high at birth then disappear, to reappear at about 10 years of age, presumably reflecting rising androgen levels. The concentration of PSA in seminal plasma is a million times greater than that in blood.

Plasma PSA concentrations do not show any circadian variation but random intraindividual fluctuation of 14% or more may occur in some individuals. After hospitalisation however, plasma concentrations may fall by 20 - 50%. The reason for this is not known. There are conflicting reports on the effect of ejaculation on plasma PSA. In young individuals it appears to result in a fall while in older men, concentrations rise. This effect lasts 24 - 48 hours. Physical exertion may also lead to a temporary increase.

Elevated plasma PSA concentrations occur in patients with carcinoma of the prostate but also in persons with benign prostatic hypertrophy (BPH), which is common, and with prostatitis, prostate ischaemia, and urinary retention. Short term elevation in acute renal failure has also been described. Like all tumour markers however, PSA is not specific for malignancy, although it is reasonably specific for prostate tissue.

A high plasma PSA does not necessarily mean carcinoma

This 76 year old man came to hospital complaining of difficulty in passing urine and a burning pain when he was able to do so. On rectal examination his prostate was enlarged and tender.

Plasma PSA was requested and the result was 40 µg/L. This level is suggestive, but not diagnostic, of malignancy. A urologist was consulted and diagnosed prostatic infection (prostatitis). He advised repeating the PSA after the infection had been treated.

Days after admission	0	2	8	24
PSA (µg/L)	40	29	8	6

The plasma PSA 4 years later was 2.1µg/L.

Figure 4.7   Plasma PSA concentrations in diagnosis

The effects of digital rectal examination is controversial, as indeed it was with prostatic acid phosphatase. The consensus is that it does produce a slight increase in plasma concentrations but not usually enough to make a clinically significant difference. Similar mild changes have been noted after cystoscopy and transurethral ultrasound examination. Plasma PSA concentrations after prostate biopsy or resection may be elevated 50 fold and take several weeks to return to baseline.

THE PSA ASSAY
The assay and standardisation of PSA has created some problems, particularly as clinicians relate the results to published decision levels. In plasma, PSA circulates in three forms: most is bound to α_2-macroglobulin and this form is not measured by current assays. The remainder is either bound to α_1-antichymotrypsin or is free. Different assays may react differently with the bound and the free forms and produce very different results. Another problem with interpretation of results has been the lack of an agreed standard with a known bound/free ratio. This has recently been agreed at 90:10, but has not yet been implemented. Even this will not eliminate variability in patients with different bound/free ratios. Furthermore, it may prove inadequate if separate assays for free and bound PSA are used.

PSA IN THE DIAGNOSIS OF PROSTATE CANCER
In cancer of the prostate the anatomical disruption allows more PSA to enter the blood

and as a result plasma PSA concentrations rise. The rise is proportional to the amount of malignant tissue present and plasma PSA measurement is the most sensitive test for prostate cancer. Screening men without symptoms offers a means of detecting and treating early disease, but the benefits of this approach have not been fully evaluated. There is vast literature on the subject and the interested reader should consult the references cited in the further reading list.

The enthusiasm surrounding the test ignores problems with both sensitivity and specificity. The commonly used upper value of plasma PSA in men without prostate pathology is 4 μg/L. At this cut-off, about a third of patients with organ-confined cancer will have normal PSA values. Sensitivity rises to about 90% in patients with disseminated disease. Coupled with this poor sensitivity in the early stage of the disease is the problem of specificity - the interpretation of the mild to moderately high value. As men age, benign prostatic hypertrophy becomes more common and, with increased prostate mass, plasma PSA concentrations increase. If the upper value of PSA in men without prostate pathology is taken as 4 μg/L, BPH is the commonest cause of values in the 4 - 10 μg/L range while values over 10 μg/L are increasingly likely to be due to malignancy.

There have been several attempts to improve the detection of cancer against this background of BPH.

- **Age-related reference ranges**
  The rise in plasma PSA that occurs with age reflects the increase of prostate mass as the inner zone expands in BPH. The original reference values were obtained in men in the 50s and 60s and are probably not appropriate for younger or older groups. The use of age-related ranges with a specificity of 95% reduces unnecessary follow-up testing by about 15% and detects more patients in the younger age group. It also reduces the overall detection rate by about 10%, mostly in the over 70 years age group.

- **PSA density**
  This concept relates plasma PSA concentrations to prostate size, determined usually by transrectal ultrasound (TRUS). There is good correlation of PSA with prostate size when measured by a highly accurate method such as magnetic resonance imaging. TRUS however is much less accurate and the cost implications are great. Hyperplastic tissue contributes about 0.04 μg/L/g. In malignancy the amount of PSA entering the blood through anatomical distortion or metastases is greater. A cut-off of 0.15 μg/L/g is proposed.

- **PSA velocity and doubling time**
  Another approach is to use each person as his own reference value and look at the trend in annual PSA concentrations. There is a steady and linear increase with BPH and any departure from this may indicate malignancy. Initial studies predict that cancer detection may be brought

forward by 10 years using this method. This means that the assay has to be stable so that results years apart are comparable. There is random variation (individual and analytical) of about 10% - 20% which means that to be sure a marginal rise is significant the test should be repeated. It may also be necessary to wait until the next year. As usually happens, a rule of thumb has been developed; a rise of more than 20% per year suggests malignancy. This sort of variation can, however, occur by chance. A similar approach has estimated the doubling time of plasma PSA which is about 4 years for localised prostate cancer and 10 years for BPH.

- **Free and bound PSA**
  The proportion of plasma PSA that is bound to α_1-antichymotrypsin (ACT) is higher in cancer ($\pm$ 90% bound) than in BPH ($\pm$ 82% bound). The reason for this is that PSA in normal and malignant tissue is secreted as a complex with ACT to a greater degree than that in hyperplastic tissue. There is considerable overlap and the most likely future use of this type of test will be to check values in the range 4 - 10 μg/L.

Several large studies have evaluated these various methods and found that all reduced the number of biopsies required by about a third, but missed about 12% of cancers. The big question hanging over plasma PSA and all these diagnostic variations is whether or not the tumours detected are clinically significant and likely to progress. Furthermore, if they are clinically significant, is early treatment going to improve outcome? Long term studies to determine this are under way but at present the answer is not known.

PSA IN PROGNOSIS AND MONITORING
Plasma PSA correlates with cancer size and extent. Staging takes a lot more into account than PSA but a few figures have emerged.

In patients with diagnosed cancer and a plasma PSA concentration:

< 4 μg/L	- most have organ confined disease (20 - 30% do not)
> 10 μg/L	- most (88%) have extracapsular spread
< 20 μg/L	- metastases are very unlikely to be detectable by bone scan
> 50 μg/L	- most (over 80%) have bone metastases.

PSA has a half life of 2 - 3 days and becomes undetectable in plasma within a month of radical prostatectomy. In such patients any subsequent rise signifies recurrence and it is in this group that supersensitive assays, in the range of 0.01 - 0.1 μg/L, show rising concentrations 3 to 5 years before clinical recurrence.

After radiation therapy the fall is slower but after a year about 80% have concentrations within the reference range. After hormone therapy concentrations fall both because of reduced androgen-dependent secretion (from normal and abnormal tissue) and tumour size reduction. Falls of more than 50% within the first month and return to the reference interval by 6 months are considered good prognostic signs.

OTHER ASPECTS OF PSA

In addition to the prostate and nearby glands, PSA, apparently identical to prostate PSA, can also be produced by apocrine glands, including sweat glands and breast. Normal breast tissue can produce PSA when stimulated by sex steroids and it is present in breast milk ($\pm$ 0.5 μg/L). About 30% of breast cancers produce it. This occurs more in progesterone receptor positive tumours, those with a more favourable prognosis. The presence of PSA in breast milk and amniotic fluid has suggested to some that it has a function as a growth regulator in fetal development and in cancer.

THYROID CANCER

There are several types of thyroid cancer as shown in Figure 4.8.

Thyroid cancer	
Well-differentiated	- follicular - papillary - mixed
Poorly-differentiated	
Other	- medullary carcinoma - lymphoma

Figure 4.8   Types of thyroid cancer

The vast majority of tumours are well-differentiated and present as a lump in the thyroid or, in about a quarter of the cases, as enlarged lymph-nodes in the neck. They are treated by surgical removal of involved tissue and have a good prognosis. Any remaining tumour is treated with radiotherapy and thyroxine replacement to suppress TSH secretion. Distant spread can be treated by administering radioactive iodine which is taken up by tumour tissue, but only if all normal thyroid tissue has been removed. Poorly differentiated carcinoma requires total thyroidectomy and radio- or chemotherapy and has a poor prognosis.

MONITORING

In patients on replacement thyroxine therapy, plasma TSH can be measured to confirm suppression. Appropriate concentrations are 0.1 - 0.4 U/L. A sensitive marker of recurrent disease in patients who have had a total thyroidectomy is thyroglobulin, the large molecule involved in storage of thyroid hormones in the colloid of the thyroid gland. It is normally present in plasma at low concentrations and increases in a range of thyroid disorders, including thyroid cancer, and so is too non-specific to be of value in diagnosis. After total thyroidectomy thyroglobulin should no longer be detectable and measurable or rising concentrations imply the presence of thyroid tissue, presumably a recurrence of the cancer. This may be made more sensitive by withdrawing replacement thyroxine therapy, which causes concentrations of TSH to rise.

The measurement of thyroglobulin is complicated by anti-thyroglobulin antibodies in the patient that often accompany thyroid disease. Depending on the assay system this may falsely raise or lower the value. There is no standard reference material.

MEDULLARY CARCINOMA
Medullary carcinoma, which represents about 5% of thyroid tumours, is a tumour of the C cells of the thyroid, cells that normally secrete calcitonin. About a quarter of these tumours are a component of multiple endocrine neoplasia type 2 (MEN2, p. 16).

Medullary carcinomas secrete calcitonin and plasma concentrations are raised in most patients. The assay is also used to detect early cancer in family members and to monitor for completeness of resection or recurrence in those who have had the tumour removed. To aid early detection in families, the measurement of calcitonin concentrations after stimulation with pentagastrin has been used. The genetic diagnosis has been considered on p. 16. These tumours may also produce CEA, peptide hormones and neuroendocrine markers. Calcitonin and CEA may be used in monitoring.

MALIGNANCY OF THE HAEMOPOIETIC AND IMMUNE SYSTEMS
Malignancies of the haemopoietic and immune systems are usually rapidly growing and have a large tumour burden. The leukaemias are monitored by peripheral blood cell counts and, when required, by marrow examination. Lymphomas are often best monitored by plasma lactate dehydrogenase activity.

Malignancies of the B cell series of the immune system include:

- myeloma (including light chain disease);
- Waldenstrom's macroglobulinaemia;
- heavy chain diseases;
- lymphomas;
- chronic lymphocytic leukaemia;
- hairy cell leukaemia.

Myeloma (myelomatosis, multiple myeloma) is a malignancy of the B cells showing differentiation towards the plasma cell. It is characterised clinically by proliferation of plasma cells in bone marrow with local and systemic symptoms (see p. 98). Waldenstrom's macroglobulinaemia affects lymph nodes rather than bone marrow.

Clinically the two conditions are dissimilar but they share the ability to secrete immunoglobulins which may be used as markers.

PARAPROTEINS AND BENCE JONES PROTEIN

The B cell normally produces immunoglobulins, each molecule of which consists of two heavy chains and two light chains. The range of antibody molecules found in health and reactive conditions differ slightly in charge and produce the diffuse gammaglobulin region on the protein electrophoretic strip. In B cell malignancy, one clone of cells proliferates and produces large amounts of a single protein that appear as a discrete band. If, on further testing, this band is shown to consist of a single heavy chain class and a single light chain type, it is called a monoclonal band or paraprotein. This is most commonly IgG or IgA in myeloma, rarely IgD, IgE or IgM. In macroglobulinaemia, IgM is produced. In the heavy chain diseases, which resemble lymphoma clinically, incomplete heavy chains are produced.

In myeloma and macroglobulinaemia there is also often production of light chains (Bence Jones protein, BJP) in excess of heavy chains: some myelomas produce only BJP. As these proteins are small (20, or 40 kD if dimers) they are filtered by the kidney and appear in the urine. If renal failure develops BJP may be detectable in serum. In myeloma the production of other immunoglobulins is frequently reduced, so on electrophoresis the paraprotein usually appears on a background of hypogammaglobulinaemia. There may be hypogammaglobulinaemia in cases where only light chains are being produced. In macroglobulinaemia by contrast, a diffuse IgG increase is often present.

The detection of a paraprotein or BJP is often the first indication of B cell malignancy which is then confirmed by bone marrow aspiration or biopsy. The plasma concentration reflects the tumour burden and the course of the disease and response to therapy can be monitored by following the paraprotein concentration in the blood or quantitating the excretion of BJP. Measurement of the paraprotein is best done by electrophoresis and densitometry. In many cases, immunological measurement of the relevant immunoglobulin provides similar information but in others, particularly IgM, values may differ greatly. This is probably due to epitopes on the monoclonal protein which react differently with the measuring antibody compared to the polyclonal standard. A change of antibody may also produce a shift in results.

β2-MICROGLOBULIN (B$_2$M)

Plasma concentrations of B$_2$M are a good indicator of the tumour mass of B cell malignancies, and are particularly useful in those that do not produce paraproteins. Plasma concentrations at presentation are an important prognostic factor, and are of value in monitoring. B$_2$M is filtered at the renal glomerulus and catabolised by the tubules so levels will also rise if renal failure develops.

OTHER MARKERS

Myeloma cell growth in the bone marrow elicits IL-6 production and this is a major growth factor for the myeloma cells. Production of the soluble IL-6 receptor also increases, as does C-reactive protein production by the liver in response to IL-6. These three substances have all been used as markers but offer no significant advantage over those discussed above.

SYMPATHETIC NERVOUS SYSTEM TUMOURS

The cells of the sympathetic nervous system develop from the primitive neural crest of the embryo along two pathways, one leading to sympathetic ganglion cells, via the neuroblast and the other to chromaffin cells, which persist in the adrenal medulla. Tumours of these cells secrete catecholamines (Figure 4.9) and measurement of these is used in diagnosis and monitoring.

Neuroblastoma is a malignant tumour that occurs in about 1 in 10,000 children, usually before the age of five years. Most arise in or around the adrenal medulla or in the posterior mediastinum and present clinically with symptoms relating to the growth of the tumour rather than the secretion of catecholamines. Some neuroblastomas regress spontaneously. Urine homovanillic acid (HVA) and/or hydroxymethoxy mandelic acid (HMMA) excretion is increased in over 85% of patients at the time of diagnosis. As the best clinical outcome is seen in children presenting in the first year of life, there have been several attempts to screen all babies at 6 months of age using HVA and/or HMMA. This does not detect all aggressive tumours.

Phaeochromocytoma is a tumour of the chromaffin cell and may present at any age. About 90% occur in the adrenal medulla, the rest along the places occupied by the primitive neural crest. About 10% are bilateral, often part of the MEN II complex (p. 16). About 10% are malignant. The symptoms relate to the secretion of catecholamines. Hypertension, sustained or paroxysmal, occurs in most patients and headache, sweating and palpitations are common. Phaeochromocytoma however accounts for only about 0.1% of patients with hypertension.

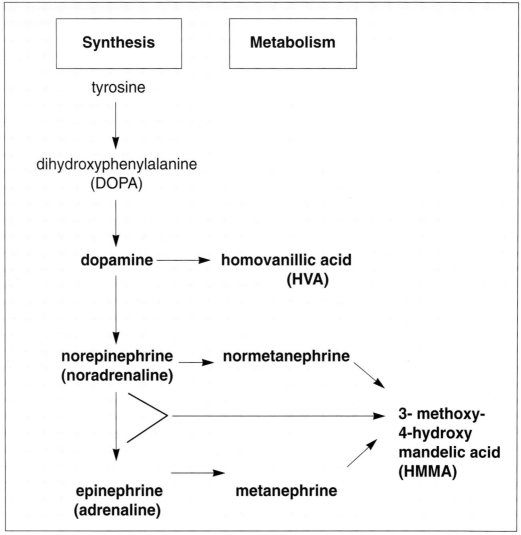

Figure 4.9   Simplified outline of catecholamine synthesis and metabolism
              indicating in bold print the substances that may be measured in
              evaluating neuroblastoma and phaeochromocytoma

The diagnosis is made by demonstrating increased catecholamine excretion and locating the tumour by imaging. Of the available tests, measurement of adrenaline and noradrenaline, or metanephrine and normetanephrine excretion in the urine are the most sensitive. The separate measurement of the two components rather than total catecholamines or total metanephrines is preferred, particularly as some tumours secrete only adrenaline. The sensitivity and specificity depend on the clinical situation (hypertension, paroxysmal hypertension or adrenal mass) and on the cut-off point. Some reference ranges include hypertensive patients who may have higher values than normotensive people and will increase specificity but lower sensitivity. The detection rate is improved if the patient is symptomatic during the collection period. HMMA, although widely used, is both less sensitive and less specific.

Plasma catecholamine assays are sensitive but require collection under strict conditions to avoid stress-induced rises. Secreted catecholamines have half lives of minutes and so periodic secretion may be missed. When plasma catecholamine concentrations are persistently high, suppression tests using clonidine have been used to distinguish between excess sympathetic nervous system activity and unregulated tumour secretion.

OTHER MARKERS

Chromogranin A is a protein that is stored and released from storage granules with catecholamines. The plasma chromogranin A concentrations have been used as a marker for both neuroblastoma and phaeochromocytoma. In both it reflects tumour size and so prognosis. It may also be elevated in patients with medullary thyroid carcinoma. Mild elevations occur in essential hypertension.

Another neuroendocrine marker, neuronspecific enolase (p. 60) may be elevated but offers no particular advantage.

CANCER OF UNKNOWN PRIMARY SITE

About 5% of all patients with cancer present with metastases without a detectable primary malignancy. Some of these will have disease that can be treated with significant clinical benefit, such as lymphoma and germ cell tumour, so the aim of investigation is to identify the type of malignancy rather than exhaustively seek the primary.

After adequate clinical evaluation the most important investigation is a good biopsy that permits adequate testing.

On light microscopy the tumour can be categorised as:

- adenocarcinoma (of variable differentiation);
- squamous carcinoma;
- poorly differentiated carcinoma;

- poorly differentiated neoplasm, which include:
  - lymphoma
  - germ cell tumour
  - neuroendocrine tumour
  - melanoma
  - sarcoma
  - other.

Further investigation includes immunoperoxidase staining whereby specific antigens are sought. Many of these will be familiar to clinical biochemists as tumour markers. Examples are:

- leucocyte common antigen for lymphoma;
- cytokeratin for carcinoma;
- neuronspecific enolase and chromogranins for neuroendocrine tumours;
- HCG and AFP for germ cell tumours;
- CEA for adenocarcinoma;
- PSA for prostate carcinoma;
- S100 protein for melanoma.

Considerable experience in performance and interpretation is needed as there are false positive and negative results, as with plasma tumour markers. DNA and chromosome analysis may detect typical changes associated with particular tumours, and electron microscopy may permit a more definite diagnosis.

The clinical presentation is variable, depending on the distribution of tumour specific clinical syndromes seen, including:

- Axillary node metastasis, usually in women, is strongly suggestive of breast cancer. Even in the absence of palpable or mammographically detectable abnormality occult breast cancer will be found in 55-75% of mastectomy specimens from these patients.
- Cervical/supraclavicular node metastasis, is usually from a primary carcinoma of the nasopharynx, oesophagus or lung. Breast cancer and melanoma may also manifest in this way.
- Skeletal metastasis in men suggests prostate cancer, and in women, breast cancer. Other primary sites include thyroid, kidney and colon.

- Peritoneal carcinomatosis in women is strongly suggestive of ovarian cancer.

- Mediastinal or retroperitoneal tumour suggests lymphoma or germ cell tumour.

- Multiple liver metastasis is most often from gastrointestinal, breast or lung cancer. Therapy is largely palliative so an exhaustive search for the primary is not warranted.

The clinical chemistry laboratory has a limited role in investigation of these patients. General biochemical tests may help establish the extent of the disease (Chapter 2) and plasma tumour markers may offer some early guidance before biopsy studies are complete.

The most useful are those for:

- adenocarcinoma   -   CEA, CA125, CA15-3
- germ cell tumour   -   AFP, HCG
- neuroendocrine tumour   -   NSE
- prostate cancer   -   PSA.

FURTHER READING

Armbruster D A. Prostate-specific antigen: biochemistry, analytical methods, and clinical application. *Clin Chem* 1993; **39:** 181-195.

Bangma C H, Kranse R, Blijenberg B G, Schröder FH. The value of screening tests in the detection of prostate cancer. *Urology* 1995; **46.**

- Part I Results of a retrospective evaluation of 1726 men. pp.773-778.

- Part II Retrospective analysis of free/total prostate-specific analysis ratio, age-specific reference ranges, and PSA density. pp. 779-784.

Bates S E. Clinical applications of serum tumor markers. *Ann Int Med* 1991; **115:** 623-638.

Bravo E L. Evolving concepts in the pathophysiology, diagnosis and treatment of pheochromocytoma. *Endocrine Reviews* 1994; **15:** 356-368.

Bunting P S. A guide to the interpretation of serum prostate specific antigen levels. *Clin Biochem* 1995; **28:** 221-241.

Burger H G, Fuller P J. The inhibin/activin family and ovarian cancer. *Trends Endocrinol Metab* 1996; **7:** 197-202.

Cole LA. β-Core fragment (β-Core, UGP, or UGF). *Tumour Marker Update* 1994; **6:** 69-75.

Cooper E H. Beta-2-microglobulin in haematological malignancy. *Tumour Marker Update* 1990; **2:** 3-5.

Cooper E H. Serum markers in leukaemia, lymphoma, multiple myeloma: recent progress. *Tumour Marker Update* 1993; **5:** 121-123.

Devine P L, McGuckin M A, Ward B G. Circulating mucins as tumor markers in ovarian cancer (review). *Anticancer Research* 1992; **12:** 709-718.

Diamandis E P, Yu H, Melegos D N. Ultrasensitive prostate-specific antigen assays and their clinical application. *Clin Chem* 1996; **42:** 853-857.

Gann P H, Hennekens C H, Stampfer M J. A prospective evaluation of plasma prostate-specific antigen for detection of prostate cancer. *JAMA* 1995; **273:** 289-294.

Graham P E, Smythe G A, Edwards G A, Lazarus L. Laboratory diagnosis of phaeochromocytoma: which analytes should we measure? *Ann Clin Biochem* 1993; **30:** 129-134.

Haglund C, Roberts P J, Kuusela P. Tumour markers in pancreatic cancer. *Tumour Marker Update* 1991; **3:** 3-6.

Hayes D F, Bast R C, Desch C E *et al.* Tumor marker utility grading system: a framework to evaluate clinical utility of tumor markers. *J Natl Cancer Inst* 1996; **88:** 1456-1466.

Jacobs I, Bast C B Jr. The CA-125 tumour-associated antigen: a review of the literature. *Human Reproduction* 1989; **4**: 1-12.

Jacobsen S J, Oesterling J E. Age-specific reference ranges for serum prostate specific antigen levels. *Jnl Clin Ligand Assay* 1995; **18**: 93-97.

Kramer B S, Brown M L, Prorok P C, Potosky A L, Gohagan J K. Prostate cancer screening: what we know and what we need to know. *Ann Int Med* 1993; **119**: 914-923.

Lamerz R. Circulating tumour markers in breast cancer. *Tumour Marker Update* 1995; **7**: 95-100.

Marrink J. TP(A) or not TP(S): What's the question? *Tumour Marker Update* 1993; **5**: 71-73.

Mettlin C, Murphy G P, Babaian R J *et al*. The results of a five-year early prostate cancer detection intervention. *Cancer* 1996; **77**: 150-159.

Pandha H S, Waxman J. Tumour markers. *Q J Med* 1995; **88**: 233-241.

Parker L. Neuroblastoma: using tumour markers to screen for childhood cancer. *Tumour Marker Update* 1993; **5**: 41-44.

Rastel D. Measurement of cytokeratin 19 fragments in serum: clinical application of a tumour marker called CYFRA 21-1. *Tumour Marker Update* 1995; **7**: 55-63.

Reibnegger G. Weiss G, Wachter H. Neopterin in malignant diseases. *Tumour Marker Update* 1992; **4**: 101-103.

Sölétormos G, Nielsen D, Schiøler V, Skovsgaard T, Dombernowsky P. Tumor marker cancer antigen 15.3, carcinoembryonic antigen, and tissue polypeptide antigen for monitoring metastatic breast cancer during first-line chemotherapy and follow-up. *Clin Chem* 1996; **42**: 564-575.

Torrens J I, Burch H B. Serum thyroglobulin measurement: utility in clinical practice. *The Endocrinologist* 1996; **6**: 125-148.

Tumor marker expert panel. Clinical practice guidelines for the use of tumor markers in breast and colorectal cancer. *J Clin Oncol* 1996; 14: 2843-2877.

Wang J Y, Tang R, Chiang J M. Value of carcinoembryonic antigen in the management of colorectal cancer. *Dis Colon Rectum* 1994; **37**: 272-277.

Weitz I C, Liebman H A. Des-γ-carboxy (abnormal) prothrombin and hepatocellular carcinoma: a critical review. *Hepatology* 1993; **18**: 990-997.

Werner M, Faser C, Silverberg M. Clinical utility and validation of emerging biochemical markers for mammary adenocarcinoma. *Clin Chem* 1993; **39**: 2386-2396.

Chapter 5

Paraneoplastic Syndromes

The paraneoplastic syndromes are clinical syndromes that develop in association with a tumour, but which are not a direct effect of the primary tumour mass or of metastases. They occur in about 7 - 15% of patients with malignancy and may be a presenting feature or develop in the course of a known malignancy. The abnormalities produced are rarely diagnostic of malignancy but their importance lies in recognising malignancy as a possible cause. Also, alleviation of the symptoms may improve the quality of life for the patient.

In most cases the syndrome is produced by something secreted by the tumour. This may be a hormone, a neurotransmitter or a cytokine and removal of the tumour usually leads to disappearance of the syndrome. In other cases the syndrome seems to be caused by the host response to the tumour, such as the development of antibodies to tumour molecules that react with similar molecules in normal tissue to produce symptoms. These do not always improve on removal of the tumour.

The best described paraneoplastic syndromes are those due to hormone secretion. Tumours of endocrine glands secrete the hormone(s) normally associated with the cell of origin of the tumour and the clinical problem is to distinguish between benign and malignant causes of the hormone excess. Factors suggesting a malignant cause include:

- very high hormone concentrations in blood or urine;
- more than one hormone being produced in excess;
- greater clinical severity.

Tumours of endocrine glands are not usually considered paraneoplastic. The main ones are listed in Figure 5.1, but will not be considered further.

Often however, a hormone appears to be produced by a tumour arising from cells which do not normally secrete it. This has been called 'ectopic' secretion but this term is too limiting. It is now apparent that peptide hormone gene expression is normally present in many tissues where the molecules may have a local paracrine or autocrine action. Many tumours produce these hormones, often in precursor form, and having less biological activity than the hormone itself. Plasma concentrations of such precursors may sometimes be sufficient to produce symptoms typical of excess of the hormone itself.

Organ	Cell	Secretion	Consequence
Anterior pituitary	• somatotroph • corticotroph • lactotroph • thyrotroph	GH ACTH prolactin TSH	acromegaly Cushing's syndrome infertility, amenorrhoea, galactorrhoea thyrotoxicosis (rare)
Thyroid	• follicular cell • C cell	thyroxine calcitonin	thyrotoxicosis (rare) none
Parathyroid	• chief cell	PTH	primary hyperparathyroidism (often severe)
Adrenal	• cortical cell • medulla	corticosteroids androgens catecholamines	Cushing's syndrome virilisation hypertension (phaeochromocytoma)
Ovary	• follicle cell • hilar cell	oestrogens androgens	endometrial hyperplasia, menorrhagia virilisation

Figure 5.1   Biochemical consequences of malignancy of endocrine glands

Many of the hormonal syndromes occur with tumours of the diffuse neuroendocrine system, a widespread system of endocrine cells scattered throughout many organs and tissues. Neuroendocrine cells are characterised by the presence of one or more of:

- hormonal peptides and amines in secretory granules;
- neuronspecific enolase;
- chromogranins;
- creatine kinase BB;
- leu-7 antigen;
- 7B2 protein.

Tumours of this system include the small cell carcinoma of the lung (SCCL), melanoma and the gastrointestinal endocrine tumours, but neuroendocrine differentiation may occur in other tumours such as prostatic carcinoma. The tumours may contain several different cell types that interact and change, so secretion patterns may vary independently of tumour progression. Because of this, hormones are not always reliable tumour markers.

The aetiological role of a tumour in a suspected hormonal syndrome can be established by:

- the presence of the syndrome in association with the tumour and remission on its removal;

- increased blood or urine levels of the relevant hormone;

- the presence of the hormone in the tumour tissue;

- higher hormone concentrations in blood leaving the tumour than in that entering it;

- mRNA for the hormone in the tumour or in cells cultivated from it.

Once the association has been confirmed however, diagnosis of future cases can be made more simply. Many syndromes have been described. This chapter will consider the best described ones and refer to some, but not all, of the others. The commonest is hypercalcaemia.

HYPERCALCAEMIA

Hypercalcaemia, a frequent and distressing complication or presenting feature of malignancy, results from increased resorption of calcium from bones and increased reabsorption from the glomerular filtrate. While it is often associated with bony metastases it has been recognised for over a century that this is not always so. In 1889 Paget (before plasma calcium measurement) noted that "a general degradation of the bones sometimes occurs in carcinoma of the breast, yet without any distinct deposit of cancer in them". In 1941 Albright suggested, in a case conference at the Massachusetts General Hospital, that a renal carcinoma might be producing parathyroid hormone. This view was held for many years until early PTH assays detected something in some, but not all, patients. It was then thought that 'parathyroid hormone-like substances' were responsible. Modern intact molecule PTH assays show that in the vast majority of cases, PTH is not responsible and that plasma concentrations of the hormone are suppressed.

PATHOGENESIS

There are several possible mechanisms of hypercalcaemia in malignancy. The commonest is increased osteoclastic bone resorption with release of calcium into the extracellular fluid. It may be classified as:

- Humoral hypercalcaemia of malignancy (HHM), where a tumour-produced agent reaches bone through the bloodstream. There may or may not be bone metastases. The tumours most often associated are squamous carcinomas, particularly of the respiratory tract, and breast, renal, ovarian and bladder cancer.

- Local osteolytic hypercalcaemia, where tumour metastases in bone act locally to promote bone resorption. The best example of this is myeloma.

The distinction is arbitrary as the same mediators may act both humorally and locally.

The main mediator of humoral hypercalcaemia is parathyroid hormone-related protein (PTHrP) which was identified in 1987 after many years of searching. It is a peptide, larger than, but with strong homology to, PTH at the N-terminal end, the region that determines PTH action. It binds to the PTH receptor in bone and the renal tubule to mimic the action of PTH i.e. release of calcium from bone and reabsorption from the glomerular filtrate, both of which increase the plasma calcium concentration. It is not a tumour-specific product: the mRNA for PTHrP is found in most fetal tissues and in many normal adult tissues, particularly the epidermis and the lactating breast. In health it probably has a paracrine or autocrine function and seems to have an important role in growth and development of the embryo. It may also be involved in placental calcium transport and in calcium mobilisation during lactation. In contrast to the relatively simple structure of the PTH gene, that of PTHrP is complex and each cell that expresses PTHrP can produce three mRNA transcripts which can produce three different length molecules (139, 141 and 173 amino acids). Which species is normally secreted is not known. In humoral hypercalcaemia of malignancy incomplete parts of the molecule have been found.

The syndrome of humoral hypercalcaemia of malignancy differs in several ways from that of primary hyperparathyroidism (1^0 HPT), the main one being that bone resorption exceeds bone formation which may actually be suppressed. This may be the result of more than one mediator acting. Co-secretion of PTHrP and interleukin 6 has been shown.

	1° HPT	HHM
Plasma calcium	↑	↑
Plasma phosphate	↓	↓
Urinary cyclic AMP	↑	↑
Plasma 1,25 diOH vitamin D	↑	↓
Bone resorption	↑	↑
Bone formation	↑	↓

Figure 5.2   Biochemical changes in primary HPT and HHM

Local osteolytic hypercalcaemia differs from humoral hypercalcaemia in that the malignant cells of secondary deposits in bone, or the cells of normal host tissue in response to the presence of tumour, produce agents that stimulate osteoclastic activity in a paracrine fashion. The distinction is not absolute as PTHrP may also act in this way and paracrine secretion, particularly in breast cancer metastases, is important. There is also some evidence that PTHrP secretion favours tumour growth and may interact with other factors with mutual potentiation of effect. Such other factors include substances produced by tumour cells, such as transforming growth factor alpha (TGFα) and tumour necrosis factor beta (TNFβ) as well as some produced by host cells such as TNFα, IL-1 and IL-6. TGFα and IL-1 have been shown to decrease bone formation. The main mediators of osteoclastic bone resorption in myeloma are TNFβ and IL-1 and 6.

Another mechanism for humoral hypercalcaemia is increased hydroxylation of 25hydroxy-vitamin D by lymphoma cells, producing 1,25 dihydroxyvitamin D excess. The hypercalcaemia in these cases results from increased intestinal absorption of calcium rather than bone resorption. 1,25 dihydroxyvitamin D concentrations in the blood are raised while PTH is suppressed. This is analogous to the hypercalcaemia in granuloma-tous disorders such as sarcoidosis, where the granuloma cells have 1α-hydroxylase activity.

Rare tumours that secrete PTH have been described.

CLINICAL FEATURES

The clinical features are those of any form of hypercalcaemia and relate to the concentra-tion of plasma calcium. Early symptoms are polyuria and polydipsia, due to the anti-AVP action of the high plasma calcium. As concentrations increase the patient feels ill, experiences nausea and abdominal pain with constipation, and may display any of a range of neurological symptoms such as confusion. Dehydration is very common and the reduced glomerular filtration aggravates the hypercalcaemia. In addition there may be other clinical features suggestive of malignancy. While hypercalcaemia may be the first evidence of a malignancy, it occurs generally late in the disease and the prognosis is poor.

DIAGNOSIS

Once hypercalcaemia has been demonstrated in suspected malignant disease, other possible causes must be eliminated. This is done on the basis of the history and clinical findings, detection of the tumour by appropriate means and by measurement of plasma PTH. Other abnormalities that may be present are a low plasma phosphate (though this is often masked by renal failure) and a raised plasma alkaline phosphatase if bone lesions are present. Hypokalaemia is frequently noted. Plasma PTH, measured by an intact molecule assay, should be suppressed and, if not, may indicate coexistent primary hyper-parathyroidism. It is important to recognise this as the prognosis is much better if the hypercalcaemia is due to primary hyperparathyroidism. Measurement of plasma PTHrP is not generally available and its role has yet to be established. Low concentrations do not exclude malignancy as a cause of the hypercalcaemia, as there are other mediators, nor do high values confirm it. Furthermore, plasma PTHrP concentrations are elevated in about 10% of patients with primary hyperparathyroidism.

Hypercalcaemia of malignancy

This 54 year old diabetic man has spent most of his time in his local pub. Recently he had become confused and had been drinking a lot of water, which was unusual for him. His drinking partner brought him to hospital.

He was found to be confused and dehydrated with clinical evidence of chronic liver disease. A blood sample showed the following results.

Plasma	Glucose	5.9	mmol/L	(fasting < 5.5)
	Sodium	135	mmol/L	(135 - 144)
	Potassium	2.6	mmol/L	(3.5 - 4.8)
	Bicarbonate	31	mmol/L	(22 - 33)
	Urea	12.3	mmol/L	(3.0 - 7.6)
	Calcium	4.39	mmol/L	(2.10 - 2.60)
	Phosphate	0.81	mmol/L	(0.8 - 1.45)
	Albumin	35	g/L	(33 - 50)

PTH was undetectable in the plasma.

He was treated by saline diuresis and mithramycin, a cytotoxic agent that, at low doses, inhibits osteoclast activity. It has been replaced for this purpose by the bisphosphonates. He was found to have a renal carcinoma and died two months later.

Comment
This is a typical story and set of results in a patient with hypercalcaemia of malignancy. The phosphate concentration, though within the reference range, is low for someone with renal failure. After rehydration the value was 0.60 mmol/L. Hypokalaemia is often seen in these patients.

Figure 5.3   Hypercalcaemia of malignancy

TREATMENT

The acute hypercalcaemic crisis is a medical emergency. The immediate treatment is to correct dehydration and increase urinary excretion of calcium by inducing a diuresis with physiological saline. Removal of the tumour or cytotoxic therapy may be possible but if not, therapy must be directed at suppressing osteoclast activity. Reduction of bone resorption may be achieved by administration of one of the bisphosphonates. These are compounds that resemble pyrophosphates and inhibit bone resorption regardless of cause. They do this by binding to the bone surface where they inhibit osteoclastic activity. In myeloma and some other haematological malignancies, steroid administration may control hypercalcaemia, possibly by reducing cytokine secretion.

Treatment of hypercalcaemia

This shows the response to infusions of disodium pamidronate (APD – a bisphosphonate) in a woman with hypercalcaemia due to disseminated breast cancer. The dose given is determined by the plasma calcium; 90 mg is the maximum recommended. This also shows the rapidity with which hypercalcaemia can develop, and recur, in patients with malignancy.

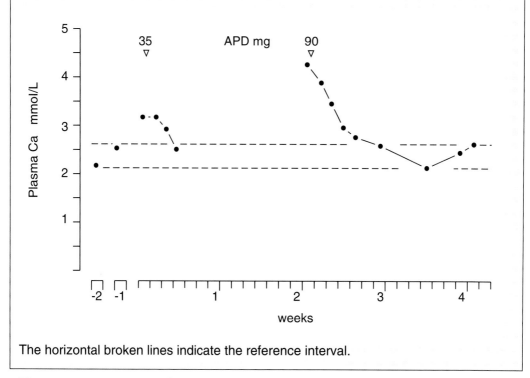

The horizontal broken lines indicate the reference interval.

Figure 5.4   **Treatment of hypercalcaemia**

THE SYNDROME OF INAPPROPRIATE ANTIDIURESIS
After hypercalcaemia, this is the syndrome most likely to be encountered.

PATHOGENESIS
Small cell cancers of the lung (SCCL) frequently produce arginine vasopressin (AVP, antidiuretic hormone) and associated peptides such as neurophysin, often in an incompletely processed form. Plasma immunoreactive AVP is raised in over half the patients with SCCL; about a third of these develop the syndrome of inappropriate antidiuresis. This term is preferable to 'the syndrome of inappropriate antidiuretic hormone secretion' as raised plasma AVP levels are not demonstrable in all cases. Furthermore, some SCCL have been shown to produce an atrial natriuretic peptide (ANP) which may also lead to hyponatraemia.

Uncontrolled tumour secretion of AVP promotes water retention, expansion of the extra-cellular fluid volume and dilutional hyponatraemia. The expanded extracellular volume leads to sodium rejection by the kidney, probably by stimulating production of ANP, and this aggravates the hyponatraemia. The reduced extracellular osmolality allows water to pass into cells. The main impact of this is on the brain where the increased intracellular volume raises intracranial pressure. The development of hyponatraemia is often so slow that intracellular compensation occurs and symptoms are absent until the plasma sodium is lower than 120 mmol/L or even 115 mmol/L. When present, they are mainly neurological and range from headache with lethargy and confusion to coma and death.

DIAGNOSIS
The diagnosis is made by demonstrating:

- hyponatraemia and hypo-osmolality;

- urine hyperosmolal to plasma;

- urine sodium greater than 20 mmol/L;

- and by excluding oedematous states, hypovolaemia, renal and adrenal insufficiency.

The aetiology is suggested by finding, and if possible removing, the tumour.

TREATMENT
The initial treatment does not differ from that for SIAD due to non-malignant causes. Water restriction corrects the hyponatraemia. If neurological symptoms are severe, isotonic or hypertonic saline may be given cautiously but this is not usually necessary. If the tumour is not amenable to therapy, the action of AVP on the renal tubule may be blocked by the drug demethylchlortetracycline (DMCT). This permits excretion of the excess water and restores the plasma sodium concentration to normal, though it has the potential to cause renal impairment and should be used with caution.

The syndrome of inappropriate antidiuresis

This 69 year old woman, who had smoked cigarettes for many years, experienced increasing shortness of breath for three weeks. She then became increasingly confused and said she felt weak and 'fuzzy headed'. On examination she was drowsy and normotensive but otherwise there were no abnormal clinical findings. Results on blood and a random urine sample were:

Plasma	Sodium	120	mmol/L	(135 - 144)
	Potassium	4.4	mmol/L	(3.3 - 4.8)
	Bicarbonate	32	mmol/L	(22 - 30)
	Chloride	81	mmol/L	(94 - 106)
	Urea	3.6	mmol/L	(3.0 - 7.6)
	Urate	0.11	mmol/L	(0.15 - 7.6)
Urine	Sodium	81	mmol/L	
	Osmolality	508	mmol/kg	

The diagnosis of the syndrome of inappropriate antidiuresis was made. Chest Xray showed a lung mass with hilar lymph node involvement. Fluid restriction was begun, and, as her confusion worsened, intravenous saline was given. As fluid restriction alone did not correct the hyponatraemia, **demethylchlortetracycline (DMCT)** was given at a dose of 900 mg a day.

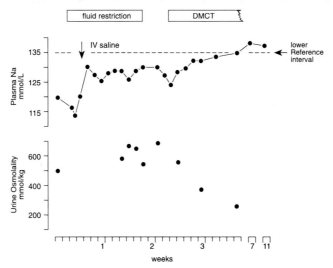

Note 1. The **hypouricaemia** on presentation. This is commonly present in SIAD and reflects the renal response to volume overload.

2. DMCT, by blocking the action of AVP, allows appropriate dilution of the urine to occur with correction of the hyponatraemia.

Figure 5.5   The syndrome of inappropriate antidiuresis

CUSHING'S SYNDROME

The uncontrolled secretion of ACTH by tumours may lead to adrenal hyperplasia and excessive cortisol secretion. The majority of tumours involved are of the neuroendocrine system, particularly small cell carcinoma of the lung (SCCL), bronchial carcinoids and phaeochromocytoma.

PATHOGENESIS

SCCL frequently expresses the genes for polypeptide hormones such as ACTH, calcitonin, vasopressin, oxytocin and gastrin-releasing peptide. Increased plasma ACTH is detectable in the blood of about half of all SCCL patients but less than 5% manifest symptoms. This may be because most of the ACTH is in the form of less active precursors. ACTH is the product of a larger molecule, pro-opiomelanocortin (POMC), the cleavage products of which in adults are ACTH and β-lipotrophin (βLPH). Many non-pituitary tissues express the POMC gene at a low level. In most cases the mRNA is shorter than normal and the hormone is not secreted. Some tumours of neuroendocrine cells produce the normal sized transcript as well as a larger one, and may secrete ACTH. However, as post-translational processing is not as efficient, precursor forms of ACTH (POMC and pro-ACTH) appear in plasma at high concentrations. Assays for these are not generally available but some ACTH assays may detect them. This secretion of large, incompletely processed forms is a characteristic of the neoplastic cell.

Another characteristic is the failure of large doses of glucocorticoids to suppress secretion, despite the presence in most of these tumours of glucocorticoid receptors and regulatory elements. It may be that transcription is initiated by a new upstream promoter (possibly by an oncogene product) that is not affected by glucocorticoid suppression. The bronchial carcinoid group (see below) are often suppressible. They may usually be distinguished from pituitary-dependent Cushing's by their failure to respond to corticotrophin-releasing hormone (CRH) as they lack CRH receptors but there are exceptions even to this. To confuse the picture further, rare cases in which the tumour secretes CRH have been described.

CLINICAL FEATURES

The clinical course of the syndrome associated with small cell carcinoma of the lung and other neuroendocrine tumours is often so rapid that the patient may not show the typical clinical features of Cushing's syndrome. ACTH and cortisol concentrations are usually very high and metabolic abnormalities, such as hypokalaemic alkalosis and glucose intolerance are prominent. There may be skin and mucous membrane pigmentation due to the melanocyte-stimulating activity of the secreted forms of ACTH. By contrast, the clinical presentation associated with bronchial carcinoid tumours may be indistinguishable from pituitary-dependent Cushing's syndrome. Hypokalaemia is prominent in this group too.

DIAGNOSIS

Once suspected, the diagnostic investigation depends on:

- Demonstrating abnormal cortisol secretion
  - excessive secretion as shown by increased daily urinary cortisol excretion.
  - lack of feedback shown by failure of plasma cortisol to suppress after an overnight or low dose dexamethasone test (1 or 2 mg taken at 2300h).
  - lack of diurnal variation between samples taken in the morning and evening.
- Identifying the cause.

This requires distinguishing Cushing's syndrome due to tumour ACTH production from that due to an adrenal or pituitary tumour by a combination of biochemical and non-biochemical tests. The biochemical tests assess the response to suppression by a larger dose of dexamethasone (2mg q.d.s. for 2 days), or to stimulation by corticotropin-releasing hormone (CRH).

Cause	P-ACTH	High dose dexamethasone test	Response to CRH
Pituitary-dependent Cushing's syndrome	high N/↑	suppression	yes
Tumour – carcinoid	high N/↑	may suppress	usually no
– SCCL	↑↑	no suppression	no
Adrenal tumour	undetectable	no suppression	no

Figure 5.6   Identifying the cause of Cushing's syndrome

Because of the difficulty in distinguishing the ACTH-producing bronchial carcinoid from pituitary-dependent disease, it is essential that all such patients have good chest imaging by tomography or CT scanning. Inferior petrosal sinus sampling may be of value in identifying the source of the ACTH.

Tumour secretion of ACTH

This 69 year old woman with mild cardiac failure had been reasonably healthy until a few months ago. Since then she had been feeling tired and increasingly weak. Her general practitioner did some tests and found a low plasma potassium. He gave her potassium tablets but, as her condition worsened, he sent her in to hospital. On admission she was clearly in cardiac failure.

Plasma	Glucose	6.3	mmol/L	(fasting < 5.5)
	Sodium	145	mmol/L	(135 - 144)
	Potassium	2.0	mmol/L	(3.5 - 4.8)
	Bicarbonate	43	mmol/L	(22 - 30)
	Chloride	91	mmol/L	(100 - 110)
	Creatinine	90	µmol/L	(50 - 120)

A chest Xray showed a large hilar mass with mediastinal lymph node enlargement. An enthusiastic registrar decided that she had a lung tumour that was secreting ACTH, and ordered further tests.

Plasma cortisol (nmol/L)

12 June	random	1070	(200 - 700)
15 June	2230h	4720	(< 200)
16 June	0900h	5380	(< 180)
(after 2 mg dexamethasone)			
Urine cortisol (nmol/24 hours)		5570	(100 - 330)

The patient died on 16th June. Autopsy showed a small cell carcinoma of the lung with widespread metastases.

Comment: This case illustrates one of the difficulties in diagnosing the tumour ACTH syndrome due to SCCL. The patient is often very ill and would be expected to have high, non-suppressible cortisol secretion. The values in this case however, exceed those usually seen in severe stress and the hypokalaemia supports the diagnosis. The presence of SCCL makes it even more likely. Plasma ACTH was not measured but would probably not have helped as it would have been high in either situation. The exotic diagnoses of enthusiastic registrars are sometimes correct.

The tumour ACTH syndrome due to bronchial carcinoid tumours presents a different problem, that of distinction from pituitary-dependent Cushing's syndrome.

Figure 5.7   Tumour secretion of ACTH

TUMOUR HYPOGLYCAEMIA

Hypoglycaemia induced by tumours other than those of pancreatic islet cells is rare and is seen mainly with large mesodermal tumours such as fibrosarcomata and mesothelioma, as well as with carcinomas of the liver and adrenal cortex. The mesodermal tumours are usually large and most are in the chest or abdomen, often retroperitoneal. The mechanism seems to be unregulated overproduction of insulin-like growth factor II (IGF-II).

Insulin-like growth factors (IGF) are single-chain polypeptides, related to insulin in structure and have shared cross-reactivities at the insulin and type 1 IGF receptor. As the normal molar plasma concentration of IGF is about 1000 times higher than that of insulin, the hypoglycaemic potential is great. It is not realised because in the plasma, IGF-I and IGF-II are bound to specific binding proteins (IGFBP), the main one being IGFBP-3. IGF, IGFBP-3 and an acid-labile subunit (ALS) form a 150 kDa complex which is too large to cross the capillary endothelial barrier. The IGFs, IGFBP-3 and ALS are synthesised in the liver, synthesis being dependent on growth hormone. Growth hormone secretion in turn can be suppressed in a feed-back loop by the IGFs.

Patients with tumour-induced hypoglycaemia show a number of abnormalities of this system. These are:

- low IGF-1 concentrations;

- normal or raised IGF-II concentrations;

- low IGF-1/IGF-II ratio;

- low IGFBP-3 concentrations;

- attenuated GH response to stimuli.

It is thought that the tumour produces IGF-II, mainly as an incompletely processed form called 'big IGF-II'. This reduces growth hormone secretion in response to physiological stimulation which in turn leads to reduced production and secretion by the liver of IGF-I, IGFBP-3 and ALS. This allows the excess IGF-II to form smaller complexes which are more available to tissue receptors.

The diagnosis in these cases is usually one of exclusion by finding suppressed insulin and C-peptide concentrations in the presence of hypoglycaemia. If assays for IGF-I, II and IGFBP-3 are available it can become more scientific. The tumours are usually obvious. Treatment with growth hormone may elevate concentrations of IGF-1, IGFBP-3 and ALS, allowing formation of the normal large complex with temporary relief of symptoms. Prednisolone may also be successful by suppressing tumour IGF-II production.

The second identified mechanism is the presence of antibodies to the insulin receptor. These bind to, and activate, the receptor in a manner analogous to thyroid stimulating antibodies in Graves' disease. Originally described in patients with diabetes and acanthosis nigricans in whom extreme insulin resistance becomes replaced by fasting hypoglycaemia, it also occurs in patients with autoimmune disease and in Hodgkin's lymphoma.

OTHER HORMONE SECRETION SYNDROMES

HCG, GYNAECOMASTIA AND THE THYROID

HCG is a peptide hormone normally produced by trophoblast cells of the placenta, but also in small quantities by the anterior pituitary. A wide variety of tumours may produce small amounts of HCG and it is a useful tumour marker (see Chapter 3). In most, this secretion has no clinical effects but in patients with trophoblast proliferation (hydatidiform mole, choriocarcinoma) or germ cell tumours, secretion may be very high. As HCG is similar in structure to other anterior pituitary peptides, such as LH and TSH, at very high plasma concentrations, cross-receptor stimulation occurs. The LH action stimulates oestrogen production and may lead, in the male, to breast enlargement (gynaecomastia). In these patients plasma oestrogen concentrations are elevated. The cross-receptor stimulation of the TSH receptor in the thyroid results in increased thyroxine secretion and biochemical or clinical thyrotoxicosis. This is in part due to the high values and in part due to the nature of the secreted HCG, which is rich in acidic variants. It has been shown that the thyrotrophic activity of HCG lies largely in these acidic forms.

HCG-induced thyrotoxicosis

This 38 year old man presented with a swelling of the left side of his neck. Fine-needle aspiration showed a poorly-differentiated tumour which was confirmed by open biopsy. The tumour cells were positive for epithelial membrane antigen and beta HCG, but negative for S100, a marker for melanoma. A diagnosis of germ cell tumour was made but no primary site could be found. On chest Xray he had multiple secondaries in the lungs. The plasma HCG concentration was 870,000 IU/L. AFP and CEA were not elevated.

Shortly after commencing chemotherapy his condition worsened and he developed a rapid pulse rate and raised blood pressure. Thyroid function tests were ordered and showed a free thyroxine concentration of > 95 pmol/L (10 - 25) with suppressed TSH. The plasma oestradiol was 2730 pmol/L (< 110).

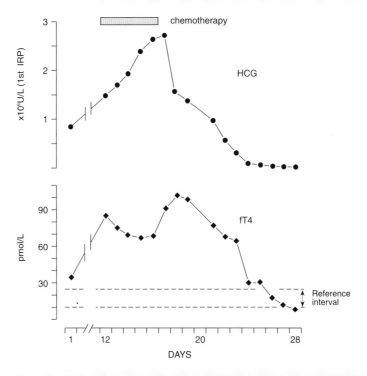

Note the initial increase in plasma HCG after starting chemotherapy and the parallel changes in plasma fT4. The thyrotoxicosis was presumed to be due to HCG stimulation of the TSH receptor.

Figure 5.8   HCG-induced thyrotoxicosis

TUMOUR-INDUCED OSTEOMALACIA

A rare and as yet unexplained syndrome is osteomalacia associated with neoplasia. Patients experience muscle weakness and bone pain in association with profound hypophosphataemia due to renal phosphate loss. The syndrome occurs with mesenchymal tumours, most commonly haemangiopericytomas, which are usually in the bone or soft tissue of the extremities. They are often small, benign and slow growing and, in many of the cases described, the osteomalacia preceded detection of the tumour by several years. The syndrome has also been described with small cell carcinoma of the lung. It is possible that the syndrome may be overlooked as low plasma phosphate concentrations are a recognised finding in patients with malignancy.

The typical biochemical findings are a low plasma phosphate with increased urinary phosphate excretion, normal plasma calcium and low plasma 1,25 dihydroxyvitamin D. Plasma PTH concentration may be raised. The finding of low 1,25 dihydroxyvitamin D in this setting is paradoxical as hypophosphataemia usually stimulates 1α-hydroxylation, which converts 25-hydroxyvitamin D to the more active form. This combination of abnormalities also occurs in X-linked hypophosphataemic rickets. The fact that removal of the tumour produces a rapid rise in 1,25 dihydroxyvitamin D, followed by return of the plasma phosphate to normal and remission of osteomalacia, suggests that a tumour-derived humoral factor may suppress 1α-hydroxylation in the proximal renal tubule. There may be other evidence of proximal tubular dysfunction such as glycosuria and aminoaciduria. The features have been reproduced experimentally using tumour extracts but the agent responsible has not been identified.

A similar form of renal phosphate wasting has been described in patients with aggressive prostate cancer.

EXTRAPITUITARY ACROMEGALY

Acromegaly may rarely be due to secretion of growth hormone (GH) or, more commonly, growth hormone-releasing hormone (GHRH). The tumours involved have been those of the neuroendocrine system including SCCL, islet cell tumours and carcinoids. Excessive GHRH secretion will result in pituitary enlargement, increased GH secretion and development of acromegaly. It is important to recognise this rare cause (<5% of cases) of acromegaly so that appropriate therapy can be given. Elevated plasma GHRH concentrations distinguish it from acromegaly due to a pituitary adenoma where plasma GHRH concentrations are suppressed.

POLYCYTHAEMIA (ERYTHROCYTOSIS)

Polycythaemia due to the secretion of erythropoeitin has been described most often in patients with renal and hepatocellular carcinomas and in those with cerebellar haemangioblastoma. It should be suspected in patients with erythrocytosis with no obvious cause and without increase in the other cellular elements in the blood.

HYPERTENSION

A very rare cause of hypertension is the secretion of renin by tumours of the renal juxta-glomerular apparatus or the neuroendocrine system. Clinically and biochemically it resembles secondary hyperaldosteronism with no obvious cause. As with many tumour secreted hormones, much of the secretion is of a precursor, in this case prorenin, an observation that is of value in diagnosis.

NEUROENDOCRINE TUMOURS OF THE GASTROINTESTINAL TRACT

Tumours of neuroendocrine cells in the gastrointestinal tract, often in the pancreas, may secrete hormones or neurotransmitters. Most are detected as a result of the syndromes produced by their secretory activity rather than their local effects, although most can metastasise. They may also contain multiple cell types and secretory patterns may change.

CARCINOID TUMOURS

These tumours arise from the enterochromaffin cells of the gut, most commonly in the ileum, appendix and rectum but they may also develop in the bronchus. Bronchial carcinoid tumours may secrete ACTH.

While the gut tumours may produce local symptoms, most are found when patients present with the carcinoid syndrome. As secretions reaching the liver via the portal system are usually inactivated there, the systemic syndrome usually only develops once metastases have developed in the liver. Bronchial tumours release their secretion directly into the systemic circulation. Clinically there are episodes of cutaneous flushing, diarrhoea and bronchospasm (wheezing) which may be provoked by stress, alcohol or particular foods. Fibrosis of the endocardium may affect the heart valves, those on the right side in patients with gut tumours, and those on the left side with bronchial carcinoids.

The main secretory product is serotonin (5-hydroxytryptamine) which is synthesised from circulating tryptophan. With extensive disease mild pellagra may develop as tryptophan is diverted from synthesis of endogenous nicotinamide, resulting in deficiency. The high concentrations of serotonin account for the intestinal hypersecretion and hypermotility that produces diarrhoea, as well as for the cardiac fibrosis. The cutaneous flushing, however, probably results from a variety of vasoactive monoamines and peptides including histamine, catecholamines and bradykinins.

The laboratory diagnosis relies on detecting excessive serotonin secretion by measuring the urinary excretion of its metabolite 5-hydroxyindoleacetic acid (5-HIAA). This assay is generally available but can have both false positive results following ingestion of fruit, nuts and a number of drugs, including paracetamol; and false negative results may occur in patients on aspirin, heparin or antidepressant therapy. An additional problem occurs with gastric carcinoids which lack aromatic L-amino acid decarboxylase and so cannot convert 5-hydroxytryptophan to serotonin. In these cases assay of total 5-hydroxyindole excretion in urine is preferable.

ISLET CELL TUMOURS

The normal pancreatic islet contains a variety of cell types, each secreting a particular hormone. Tumours of these cells produce characteristic syndromes and are not infrequently part of the MEN syndromes. The main ones are:

Insulinoma, a tumour of B cells, secretes insulin in an uncontrolled manner and causes fasting hypoglycaemia. The investigation of hypoglycaemia is beyond the scope of this book. The characteristic findings are elevated insulin and C-peptide concentrations in the presence of hypoglycaemia.

Gastrinoma, which may also develop from G cells in the duodenum, secretes gastrin. This produces hyperchlorhydria with peptic ulceration and diarrhoea (Zollinger-Ellison syndrome). The diagnosis is made by measuring plasma gastrin concentrations. If elevated, the condition may be distinguished from other causes of hypergastrinaemia by an exaggerated rise of plasma gastrin in response to the administration of secretin.

Glucagonoma, a tumour of A cells, produces hyperglycaemia. Typically, but not invariably, patients have a characteristic skin lesion termed erythema necrolytica migrans. Other features include anorexia, glossitis, diarrhoea, anaemia and venous thrombosis. Plasma glucagon concentrations are raised.

Somatostatinoma, a tumour of D cells, secretes somatostatin and results in diabetes mellitus, diarrhoea and steatorrhoea, and biliary calculi.

The Verner-Morrison syndrome, or WDHA syndrome, results from secretion of vasoactive intestinal peptide and manifests as **W**atery **D**iarrhoea, **H**ypokalaemia and **A**chlorhydria.

Pancreatic islet cell tumours may also secrete pancreatic polypeptide (PP). This may be associated with a skin condition called necrolytic erythema.

In addition, islet cell tumours may produce AVP resulting in the syndrome of inappropriate antidiuresis, ACTH or CRF resulting in Cushing's syndrome, or GHRH resulting in acromegaly.

SYSTEMIC EFFECTS OF MALIGNANCY OF THE IMMUNE SYSTEM

Tumours of B cells may secrete immunoglobulin molecules or fragments which are useful tumour markers (p. 72). In certain cases these secreted proteins may themselves produce symptoms. If paraprotein levels are very high, particularly IgM paraproteins, hyperviscosity of the blood and vascular insufficiency may occur. Hyperviscosity may be even worse if the paraprotein has cryoglobulin characteristics. This may also present problems in the laboratory when aspirating the viscous sample for analysis or if the protein precipitates out on contact with reagents. Excess light chains (Bence Jones protein) are filtered at the renal glomerulus and may precipitate in tubules to produce renal failure. They may also pass into the extravascular tissue where, in combination with serum amyloid A protein, deposition as amyloid occurs. This may involve any tissue but the consequences are most severe in the heart, kidney and liver with subsequent organ failure. There is also an association between paraproteinaemia, particularly IgM, and neuropathy, possibly due to neural infiltration by the paraprotein.

Patients with myeloma have suppression of non-paraprotein immunoglobulins which predisposes them to recurrent infections. Cultures of myeloma cells have been shown to produce a factor that suppresses B cell immune function but it has not been identified. Similar immunoglobulin deficiency is a feature of many lymphomas and, rarely, is seen in patients with solid tumours.

OTHER SYNDROMES

There are several other categories of paraneoplastic syndromes which are unlikely to involve the clinical biochemist. They are considered briefly to emphasise the wide ranging effects of malignancy.

THYMOMA

Tumours of the thymus gland rival small cell lung carcinoma in the variety of paraneoplastic syndromes they can produce. The most common is myasthenia gravis, (10 - 15% of patients) in which there is muscle weakness and easy fatiguability. It is associated with antibodies to the acetylcholine receptor and other molecules in muscle. Thymectomy does not usually result in improvement. About 5% of patients may also develop pure red cell aplasia, with severe normochromic normocytic anaemia, due to an IgG inhibitor of erythroblastic growth. About a third of such patients improve after thymectomy. About 10% develop immunoglobulin deficiency (hypogamma-globulinaemia), the pathogenesis of which is not known. Removal of the thymoma does not necessarily result in remission suggesting that, as in the case of myasthenia gravis, it is a host response factor rather than a tumour secretion that is the cause.

NEUROMYOPATHIC SYNDROMES

The central and peripheral nervous system may be involved in malignancy by direct tumour involvement, as a result of chemotherapy or as a paraneoplastic syndrome. A variety of such syndromes have been described, and include peripheral neuropathy, myasthenia, subacute encephalomyelitis and subacute cerebellar degeneration. Most are associated with small cell cancer of the lung or ovarian and breast cancer. They are often severe, develop subacutely and may be characteristic, though not diagnostic of malignancy. Many of these conditions are associated with the presence of antibodies in the plasma and, in central nervous system involvement, the cerebrospinal fluid. These antibodies react with both tumour and neurological tissue. For example, antibodies found in the Lambert-Eaton syndrome, which is characterised by muscle weakness, are directed against the voltage-sensitive calcium channels in the nerve terminal. Proof that these antibodies are causal is lacking for most of the syndromes but their presence should suggest an underlying malignancy.

DERMATOLOGICAL SYNDROMES

A number of skin symptoms and signs may be associated with malignancy. These range from conditions such as acanthosis nigricans, which in the adult may indicate gastrointestinal malignancy with some certainty, to others such as dermatomyositis where the association is weaker. The pathophysiological link between the tumour and the skin condition has not been defined.

FURTHER READING

Cascino T L. Neurological complications of systemic cancer. *Med Clin N Amer* 1993; **77:** 265-278.

Daughaday W H, Deuel T F. Tumour secretion of growth factors. *Endocrin Metab Clin N Amer* 1991; **20:** 539-563.

Gutierrez G E, Poser J W, Katz M S, Yates A J P, Henry H L, Mundy G R. Mechanisms of hypercalcaemia of malignancy. *Balliere's Clin Endocrin Metab* 1990; **4:** 119-138.

Hewison M, Karmali R, O'Riordan J L H. Tumour induced osteomalacia. *Clin Endocrin* 1992; **37:** 382-384.

Marks V, Teale J D. Tumours producing hypoglycaemia. *Diabetes/Metabolism Reviews* 1991; **7:** 79-91.

Morgenthaler T I, Brown L R, Colby T V, Harper C M, Coles D T. Thymoma. *Mayo Clin Proc* 1993; **68:** 1110-1123.

Moses A M, Scheinman S J. Ectopic secretion of neurohypophyseal peptides in patients with malignancy. *Endocr Clin N Amer* 1991; **20:** 489-506.

Mundy G R. Ectopic production of calciotropic peptides. *Endocrin Metab Clin N Amer* 1991; **20:** 473-487.

Streeten D H P, Moses A M. The syndrome of inappropriate vasopressin secretion. *The Endocrinologist* 1994; **3:** 353-358.

Wajchenberg B L, Mendonca B B, Liberman B, Pereira M A A, Carneiro P C, Wakamatsu A, Kirschner M A. Ectopic adrenocorticotropic hormone syndrome. *Endocrine Reviews* 1994; **15:** 752-787.

Zapf J. IGFs: function and clinical importance. 3. Role of insulin-like growth factor (IGF) II and IGF binding proteins in extrapancreatic tumour hypoglycaemia. *J Int Med* 1993; **234:** 543-552.

Chapter 6

The Treatment Of Cancer

The ideal of cancer treatment is to achieve cure by the removal and destruction of all malignant cells, in particular tumour stem cells which are capable of reconstituting the cancer population. In some cancers, such as testicular tumours, these curative efforts are remarkably successful but in the vast majority, cure is a more difficult undertaking. Many patients enter complete remissions, with no evidence of detectable tumour cells by clinical, radiological or biochemical means, but in a significant proportion, even if initial treatment appears successful tumour cells ultimately regrow to a clinically detectable tumour, resulting in relapse. Many of these patients will die of their disease despite repeated attempts at achieving further remissions and cures.

STAGING
Before cancer treatment begins, all patients undergo a process of clinical and laboratory investigations called staging in order to:

- establish the diagnosis;

- determine the local extent of the cancer with particular reference to the possibility of surgery;

- determine whether metastatic disease is present.

Staging allows the definition of prognostic groups although, in some diseases, other factors also influence prognosis. The most widely used staging system is the TNM classification which defines a number of staging classes according to the size of the tumour (T), the extent of nodal involvement (N) and the presence or absence of metastases (M). For example, a woman with a 1.5 cm breast cancer with uninvolved axillary lymph nodes and no evidence of metastases is classified as $T_1N_0M_0$ and has Stage I disease which has a good prognosis following surgery. On the other hand, a woman with a 3.0 cm breast cancer and the involvement of ten axillary lymph nodes by cancer but without distant metastases is classified as $T_2N_1M_0$ (Stage II disease) and has a worse prognosis following surgery. There are other agreed systems of staging for particular tumours. Accurate staging is a combined effort of the clinician (history and physical examination), radiologist (Xrays, CT scans, isotope scans etc.), biochemical and haematological pathologists (tumour markers) and the histopathologist and surgeon (tumour biopsy and resection).

TREATMENT OPTIONS

The treatment of malignant disease is a combined effort on the part of many disciplines. Surgery was the earliest form of cancer therapy and is still the most widely used. It usually forms the first line of attack and includes diagnostic biopsies, staging and, ultimately, therapy by resection of part or all of the tumour mass. This allows the pathologist to confirm that the tumour has been fully excised and confirms the nature of the disease. Unfortunately, as the surgeon cannot detect the microscopic extensions that characterise most cancers, it is usually necessary to resect the tumour with a wide margin of normal tissue in order to achieve total tumour clearance. Perhaps the greatest shortcoming of surgery is its inability to treat cancer that has metastasised widely throughout the body. In most cancers, surgical treatment is usually followed by additional forms of therapy, called adjuvant therapy, which may include chemotherapy, radiation therapy, hormonal therapy, immunotherapy or a combination of these. For several tumours, carcinoma of the oesophagus and rectum for example, concomitant chemoradiotherapy has been shown to be superior to either treatment administered alone. In other situations, surgery is delayed until radiation therapy and/or chemotherapy, has been administered first; this is often referred to as neoadjuvant or induction treatment.

Radiation therapy was applied in the treatment of cancer within one year of the discovery of Xrays by Wilhelm Roentgen in November 1895. It involves the application of Xrays or gamma rays delivered from external sources, or by the implantation of a radiation source within the body in order to irradiate the cancerous tissue. Different types of radiation have different abilities to cause biological damage and act through a number of mechanisms to effect cellular death. The most important mechanism is direct DNA damage which results in single- or double-strand breaks, alteration or loss of bases and DNA strand cross-linking. If the cell cannot repair this damage it undergoes programmed cell death (apoptosis). In addition radiation damages cellular macromolecules and interferes with specific cellular biochemical processes. Following radiation therapy, the cell's capacity to proceed through cell division is impaired; this effect may be seen at relatively low doses of radiation. As normal cells are much more successful in repairing radiation injury than cancer cells, it is possible to apply radiation therapy to the cancerous growth, as well as surrounding normal tissues, without sacrificing the patient's ability to function. This approach is particularly successful in treatment of early stages of carcinoma of the cervix, laryngeal carcinoma and Hodgkin's disease. Thus, unlike surgery, radiation therapy can successfully treat the tumour's microscopic extensions, but like surgery it is unable to treat widespread metastatic disease. Furthermore, the ability to deliver radiation therapy is limited by the tolerance of normal tissue to radiation and by the presence within tumours, especially large ones, of a significant proportion of hypoxic cells which are resistant to radiation therapy.

Hormonal therapy manipulates the body's endocrine system to treat cancers. This form of therapy is particularly effective in two of the commonest cancers, breast and prostate. In many patients with these cancers, the growth of tumour cells is regulated by endogenous hormones. This sensitivity can be exploited therapeutically by the administration of exogenous hormones e.g. medroxyprogesterone in breast cancer, or substances which deprive the cancer cell of hormones, e.g. tamoxifen in breast cancer or androgen-blocking drugs in prostate cancer. This form of therapy is relatively free of side effects and may be effective for remarkably long periods of time; ultimately hormone-independent cells that are present or that arise within the tumour will begin to proliferate. Unlike chemotherapeutic agents which are usually administered in a cyclical fashion, the effectiveness of hormonal therapy depends on long-term exposure to the drug.

Therapy with biologic agents is the newest form of therapy for malignant diseases. This diverse category includes anticancer vaccines, monoclonal antibodies, cytokines, angiostatic factors, antimetastatic agents and growth factors. These agents were originally believed to be highly specific, well-tolerated and simple means of cancer therapy; unfortunately significant toxicities have been observed for many, and their widespread clinical application has, with the singular exception of haematopoietic growth factors such as G-CSF, GM-CSF and erythropoietin, not eventuated. Nevertheless, many biologic agents promise to transform the practice of cancer therapy and will undoubtedly be used more widely in the future.

CHEMOTHERAPY

The form of treatment that most involves the clinical biochemist is chemotherapy. The term refers to the systemic administration of anticancer drugs in order to deliver these agents throughout the entire body via the blood circulation. While hundreds of compounds are used in chemotherapy of cancers, they all share a common theme; they are designed to interfere with DNA replication and to prevent cell division and multiplication.

They do this in a number of ways (Figure 6.1) and any one drug may have more than one mechanism of action. These include:

- **Inhibition of DNA synthesis** by inhibiting enzymes involved in the synthesis of, for example, deoxyribonucleotides (ribonucleotide reductase) or, more specifically, deoxythymidilate (thymidilate synthase and dihydrofolate reductase), key steps in DNA synthesis.

- **Prevention of DNA elongation**, for example by inhibiting DNA polymerase.

- **Prevention of DNA replication** by damaging the DNA so it cannot function as a template for a new strand or causing misreading of the template. This may involve binding of the drug to DNA (alkylating agents), inhibition of the topoisomerases, enzymes that control helix formation, or insertion of the drug into the DNA strand (intercalating agents), leading to unwinding of the helix.

Chemotherapeutic agents

Antimetabolites - enzyme inhibitors

These drugs inhibit enzymes involved in the synthesis of DNA or its component molecules. The principal enzyme inhibited is shown but many of these agents have several actions.

5-Fluorouracil	- thymidilate synthase
Methotrexate	- dihydrofolate reductase
Cytosine arabinoside (ara-C)	- DNA polymerase
6-Mercaptopurine, 6-Thioguanine	- phosphoribosylpyrophosphate aminotransferase
Deoxycoformycin	- adenosine deaminase
Hydroxyurea	- ribonucleotide reductase
Fludarabine	- ribonucleotide reductase
(Cladribine) 2-Chlorodeoxyadenosine	- ribonucleotide reductase
Gemcitabine (2,21 -Difluoro-2-deoxycytidine)	- ribonucleotide reductase

DNA template damaging agents

Alkylating agents - these agents form covalent bands with molecules in DNA and prevent replication.
   Nitrogen mustards - mechlorethamine, cyclophosphamide, ifosfamide, melphalan, chlorambucil
   Nitrosoureas - carmustine (BCNU), lomustine (CCNU), semustine (methyl CCNU), streptozotocin
   Platinum compounds - cisplatin, carboplatin
   Others - thiotepa, busulfan, procarbazine, mitomycin-C, dacarbazine, hexamethylmelamine.

Topoisomerase inhibitors - these interfere with the topoisomerases, enzymes that preserve the DNA helix during replication
Topoisomerase I inhibition
   Camptothecins - irinotecan, topotecan
Topoisomerase II inhibition
   Antibiotics - doxorubicin, epirubicin, daunorubicin, mitoxantrone, idarubicin
   Podophyllotoxins - etoposide, teniposide.
Intercalating agents - these insert into the DNA strand and lead to unwinding.
   Dactinomycin, mithramycin
Uncertain mechanism
   Bleomycin

Figure 6.1   Chemotherapeutic agents

Plant-derived agents

These agents interfere with microtubular function

Vinca alkaloids (spindle poison) - vincristine, vinblastine, vinorelbine
Taxanes (tubulin polymerisation) - paclitaxel, docetaxel

Hormonal agents

These agents modify the growth of hormone-dependent tumours

Hormones – oestrogens, androgens, progestins, corticosteroids
Antihormones – tamoxifen, aminogluthethimide, flutamide, aromatase inhibitors

Miscellaneous

mitotane - used in adrenal carcinoma. It inhibits corticosteroid synthesis.
L-asparaginase - this depletes serum asparagine on which certain tumour cells rely.
estramustine - an alkylating agent coupled to oestrogen to facilitate uptake.

Figure 6.1   Chemotherapeutic agents (continued)

- Interference with the function of the microtubules, dynamic structures that transport metabolites, move intracellular organelles and form the spindle that pulls the chromosomes apart at cell division. These microtubules consist of tubulin and are normally assembled and disassembled rapidly. Drugs such as the vinca alkaloids disrupt the tubule assemblies, while the taxanes promote stable but abnormal assemblies of tubulin, so reducing the amount available for normal microtubule synthesis.

Some of these agents are cell cycle specific (Figure 6.2) as they interfere with reactions occurring at specific points in the cycle. Others are non-cell cycle specific and their effect is exponentially related to the dose and to the rate of cell proliferation. Relative specificity for one or more phases of cell cycle leaves a partly synchronised population of cells surviving after treatment. Theoretically, cells in Go would be recruited into the population of surviving dividing cells, resulting in increased cell kill with subsequent cycles. In human tumours however, the heterogeneity of tumour populations, drug distribution, and poor cell-cycle synchronisation make this principle difficult to apply in practice.

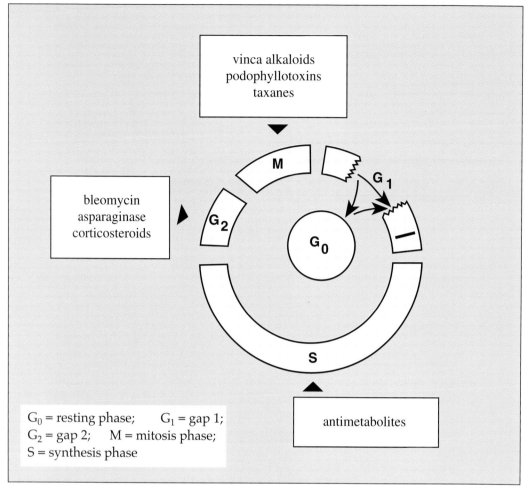

Figure 6.2   Cell cycle-specific chemotherapeutic agents

DRUG REGIMENS

The first chemotherapeutic drugs were developed in the 1940s and often proved inadequate when administered individually or in sequence. In part this was due to the development of resistance to the agents, much as bacteria develop resistance to antibiotics. Clinical trials over the next 20 years conclusively established the principle of multi-agent chemotherapy, with several drugs administered together and for a number of cycles, separated by fixed time periods. The drugs chosen as part of these regimens usually act through different mechanisms to interfere with DNA replication and have non-overlapping toxicities, thus allowing their administration at well defined doses. Many malignancies became curable through the development of such multi-agent regimens, Hodgkin's disease, testicular cancers and acute lymphoblastic leukaemia being just some of the best known examples.

Drug resistance is still a major problem. There are probably several mechanisms. For example, tumour cells overexpressing P-glycoprotein (the product of the MDR1 gene) actively transport a range of anticancer drugs out of the cell. Understanding and identification of such pathways may allow the development of therapy to circumvent drug resistance.

Through the process of clinical trials and experience in the clinic, certain drug combinations have become established as the 'gold standard' in cancer therapy. Some of these drug regimens are listed in Figure 6.3.

Regimen	Drugs	Disease treated
MOPP	Mechlorethamine, Vincristine, Procarbazine, Prednisolone	Hodgkin's disease
CHOP	Cyclophosphamide, Doxorubicin, Vincristine, Prednisolone	Non-Hodgkin's lymphoma
ICE	Idarubicin, Ara-C, Etoposide	Acute leukaemia
CMF	Cyclophosphamide, Methotrexate, 5-Fluorouracil	Breast cancer
AC	Doxorubicin, Cyclophosphamide	Breast cancer
PEB	Cisplatin, Etoposide, Bleomycin	Testicular cancer
VIP	Ifosfamide, Cisplatin, Etoposide	Testicular cancer

Figure 6.3   Some combination chemotherapy regimens

HIGH DOSE CHEMOTHERAPY AND STEM CELL SUPPORT

In an attempt to increase the cure rate of cancers, high doses of chemotherapy drugs may be given to patients with a wide range of malignancies. Since with many agents the dose is limited by myelosuppression, high doses of these agents can only be given if the patient's haematopoietic stem cells are replaced with either the patient's own cells, collected and stored before therapy (autologous transplantation) or those of another individual with identical or similar tissue recognition antigens (allogeneic transplantation).

The sources of haematopoietic stem cells include bone marrow, peripheral blood and the cord blood of neonates. Peripheral blood stem cells (PBSC) are usually collected after stimulation with haematopoietic growth factors sometimes with pulses of chemotherapy and are at least as effective as bone marrow-derived stem cells. PBSC are used extensively both in autologous and allogeneic transplants. With improvements in supportive care techniques such as the use of haematopoietic growth factors following transplantation, the duration of hospital stay and thus the cost has been greatly reduced. Many centres perform several autologous transplants in quick succession in a further attempt to improve dose intensity of the chemotherapy with many patients being treated as outpatients.

The timing of dose intensification varies according to the type and stage of disease treated.

High dose chemotherapy may be used:

- As primary therapy (non-Hodgkin's lymphoma). The potential advantage of this approach is the administration of high dose chemotherapy before drug resistance is induced by standard chemotherapy.

- As adjuvant therapy (non-Hodgkin's lymphoma, Stage II and III breast cancer, myeloma). Treatment is administered at the time of minimal disease load but early in the course of the disease.

- After failure of standard therapy (haematological malignancies, non-Hodgkin's lymphoma, Hodgkin's disease, breast cancer, testicular cancer).

- In refractory disease (haematological malignancies, non-Hodgkin's lymphoma, Hodgkin's disease). A few patients can still be cured by this approach, validating the hypothesis that high dose chemotherapy can overcome treatment resistance in some patients.

The chemotherapeutic agents administered to the patients are usually alkylating agents or platinum drugs which can be used at high doses without life-threatening non-myelosuppressive side effects. Side effect are however frequent and include mucositis, enteritis and rarely hepatotoxicity and nephrotoxicity. The greatest dangers to the patient remain infectious complications and severe immunosuppression, particularly in patients treated with allogeneic transplantation, who experience the syndrome of acute and/or chronic graft-versus-host disease.

Despite these problems, significant costs, numerous morbidities and a mortality rate that ranges between 1-20%, the use of high dose chemotherapy with haematopoietic stem cell support continues to increase rapidly. The eventual use of this approach will depend on the results of randomised clinical trials but for a number of haematological malignancies it is now standard form of therapy.

DRUG TOXICITY

Toxicity to normal tissues limits both the dose and frequency of drug administration. Tissues that have a high proliferative rate (bone marrow, skin, gastrointestinal mucosa, testis, ovary, hair follicles) rely on stem cell renewal for expansion and maintenance of the short lived differentiated cell population. Under normal conditions, stem cells are less likely to be in cycle than the cells in the expanding, differentiated population and are therefore less likely to be affected by cell-cycle specific chemotherapeutic agents. On the other hand, non cell-cycle specific agents are capable of damaging both the rapidly proliferating cell population and normal stem cells. Tissues that have a low proliferative rate (lung, kidney, liver, endocrine glands, vascular endothelium) and those that have little or no proliferation (bone, cartilage, nerve and muscle) are relatively protected against cell-cycle specific chemotherapeutic agents.

Bone marrow is frequently affected during chemotherapy because of its high rate of cell production and differentiation. A constant production of progenitor cells is needed from the pluripotent stem cell pool in order to replenish cells in the myelocytic, megakaryocytic and erythroid lineages. The rate of production, differentiation and maturation as well as the functional aspects of the blood cells is under the control of endogenous growth factors. Under normal conditions the pluripotent stem cells proliferate very slowly, the lineage-specific precursors proliferate more rapidly, while the committed, well-differentiated cells entering the circulation do not proliferate at all.

The effect of chemotherapy is therefore greatest on the rapidly proliferating cells in the early parts of the maturation series with little or no effect on the slowly proliferating stem cells, or the mature, non-proliferating cells in the circulation. Blood counts remain within normal limits for several days following chemotherapy as the mature surviving cells continue to differentiate, and then fall rapidly when the supply of cells is suddenly interrupted. This effect is greatest for the short lived granulocytes (lifespan of 1-2 days), less noticeable for platelets (lifespan of 5-7 days) and unusual for red cells (lifespan of about 120 days). The number of mature granulocytes typically decreases 7-10 days following therapy with drugs such as doxorubicin or cyclophosphamide, but this may occur earlier or later for other drugs. The optimum interval between treatment cycles, usually 21-28 days for most cytotoxic drugs, allows the recovery of the proliferating elements as well as the more slowly proliferating cellular subpopulations. Recent availability of haematopoietic growth factors such as G-CSF, GM-CSF, IL-3, erythropoietin and megakaryocyte-derived growth factor has permitted the use of higher doses of cytotoxic drugs, or administration at more frequent intervals.

Administration of certain drugs (busulfan, BCNU) causes injury to the pluripotent stem cell pool and repeated courses of therapy or treatment with high doses of these drugs may have irreversible effects on the ability of stem cell to repopulate, resulting in prolonged periods of cytopenias and bone marrow hypoplasia or aplasia.

Ulceration of the gastrointestinal tract mucosa (mucositis) is a common side effect of many cytotoxic drugs, both cell-cycle specific and non-specific. The use of antimetabolites such as 5-Fluorourocil (5FU), cytosine arabinoside or methotrexate results in a predictable injury observed 5-7 days after drug administration and affecting predominantly the rapidly dividing cells in the intestinal crypts. In most instances, this injury is mild and self-limiting and produces abdominal discomfort, diarrhoea, cramping, nausea and oropharyngeal mucositis. Other agents such as doxorubicin, cyclophosphamide and melphalan increase the severity of mucosal damage when used in combination and affect not only the proliferating cells but the intestinal crypt stem cells as well. With the increased use of haematopoietic growth factors in chemotherapeutic regimens, intestinal injury has become the main dose-limiting aspect.

Partial or complete hair loss (alopecia) occurs because of the effect of cytotoxic drugs on proliferating cells of the hair follicle. For many agents (doxorubicin, cyclophosphamide), the effect is rapid and virtually universal, beginning within 2-3 weeks of the treatment. Other agents (vinca alkaloids, 5FU) cause little or no hair loss. Hair regrowth usually occurs following chemotherapy, but at a slow rate.

Gonadal function may be impaired. Both spermatogenesis and formation of ovarian follicles involve rapid cellular proliferation and are therefore affected by chemotherapeutic agents. Sperm production falls rapidly following one or two cycles of chemotherapy with alkylating agents, as well as others, and may not recover on cessation of therapy. Chemotherapy usually results in temporary or permanent cessation of menstrual periods and the development of menopausal symptoms in pre-menopausal women. This is accompanied by elevated plasma LH and FSH and low oestradiol concentrations.

Sperm banking is commonly offered to men prior to chemotherapy for curable diseases, and embryo storage and recently, egg storage facilities, have become available for women who may wish to conceive in the future. This effect is age-dependent and is more commonly seen with prolonged courses of non-cycle specific chemotherapy (alkylating agents) or high dose chemotherapy.

Drug-induced nausea and vomiting is a common side effect of chemotherapy and one which patients fear most often. It is usually observed in the first few hours (rarely days) of chemotherapy, and is due to a complex interplay of the drug effect on the vomiting centre in the brainstem, on other areas of the nervous system, as well as on the gastrointestinal tract. Some drugs, such as cisplatin and mechlorethamine, are virtually universal in causing severe nausea and vomiting while others, such as vincristine, do not do so. Nausea and vomiting may be compounded by biochemical disturbances such as hypercalcemia and hyponatremia, which are common in cancer patients. Modern antiemetic regimens using $5HT_3$ antagonists, such as ondansetron and tropisetron, usually in combination with other agents such as corticosteroids (dexamethasone), have revolutionised chemotherapy by their dramatic effects on the frequency, severity and duration of post-chemotherapy nausea and vomiting.

RENAL AND ELECTROLYTE COMPLICATIONS

Many chemotherapeutic agents are toxic to the kidney, especially to the tubular epithelium and the epithelial lining of the urinary tract. The incidence varies from almost universal in patients treated with high dose cytosine arabinoside to uncommon with drugs such as the antitumour antibiotics. Even related drugs may vary in their toxicity. Cisplatin for example, causes renal tubular dysfunction and, at higher doses, results in nephrotoxicity that is dose limiting; carboplatin on the other hand produces nephro-toxicity far less often.

Renal function in patients with malignancy may also be compromised by other factors such as hypovolaemia, hypercalcaemia, Bence Jones proteinuria, hyperuricaemia or other drugs. The occurrence of tumour lysis during chemotherapy (p. 116) may also cause significant renal dysfunction.

The main abnormalities produced and the drugs responsible are:

- Acute oliguric renal failure
  - cisplatin, carboplatin
  - ifosfamide
  - methotrexate
  - mithramycin.

- Magnesium wasting is seen in patients being treated with cisplatin which is excreted by the kidney. It is due to proximal tubular damage and commonly produces hypomagnesaemia which, if uncorrected may lead to hypocalcaemia. The dose of cisplatin may be adjusted according to the creatinine clearance, and patients may be monitored by this.

- Dilutional hyponatraemia may occur in patients being treated with cyclophosphamide. It resembles the syndrome of inappropriate antidiuresis but is probably due to a direct toxic action on the distal renal tubules and collecting ducts which impairs water excretion. It develops soon after therapy begins and is self limiting, lasting usually 12 - 24 hours. The syndrome may also occur with other agents such as vincristine and vinblastin.

- Renal tubular acidosis may occur with 5-azacytidine.

- Glomerular damage presenting as renal failure or proteinuria may occur in patients on streptozotocin or gallium nitrate.

- Vascular damage with hypertension and development of the haemolytic-uraemic syndrome, may occur with mitomycin C therapy. This may produce anaemia and raised plasma LD activity.

Cyclophosphamide-induced hyponatraemia

This 76 year old woman developed generalised abdominal pain and jaundice. Her liver was enlarged and radiological studies showed dilated bile ducts, confirming extrahepatic obstruction. At laparotomy she was found to have a mass of enlarged lymph nodes obstructing the common bile duct. Histology showed this to be lymphoma.

Chemotherapy with vincristine, cyclophosphamide and prednisolone, together with allopurinol, was started. To protect the kidneys, she was given 3 litres of fluid a day.

A day later she became confused and was found to have a plasma sodium of 114 mmol/L. The urinary osmolality of 231 mmol/kg was the same as that of plasma, indicating impaired diluting ability. Fluid intake was reduced and the sodium returned to normal.

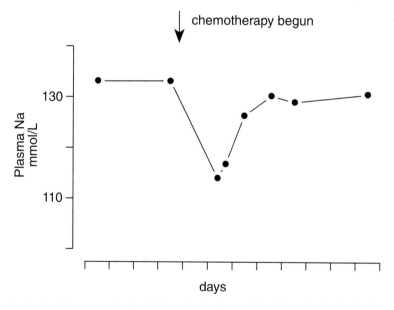

This illustrates a tubular effect of chemotherapy, probably cyclophosphamide, on the renal tubule. The impaired diluting ability leads to water retention and this is compounded by the giving of fluids to try to induce a diuresis to protect the kidneys. It is usually of short duration and does not necessitate cessation of chemotherapy.

Figure 6.4   Cyclophosphamide-induced hyponatraemia

- Haemorrhagic cystitis may occur in patients being treated with the oxasaphosphorine alkylating agents ifosfamide and cyclophosphamide. It is caused by a metabolite, acrolein. Administration of mesna (2-mercaptoethane sulphate), which neutralises acrolein, protects the urothelium and allows the use of very high doses of these drugs during procedures such as stem cell transplantation.

In many cases, nephrotoxicity may be minimised by avoiding toxic doses and maintaining a good urine output.

HEPATIC COMPLICATIONS

The liver is a major site of drug metabolism and is therefore susceptible to damage by chemotherapeutic agents or their metabolites. Biochemical evidence of cell damage is common during chemotherapy but is usually mild and asymptomatic and does not require cessation of therapy. It may be that the long cell cycle of the normal liver (a year or more) makes it less susceptible to most chemotherapeutic agents.

The full spectrum of pathological changes may be seen in biopsy specimens. The commonest is damage to cells around the hepatic veins (centrilobular), the zone primarily involved in drug metabolism, which produces mild to moderate elevations in plasma transaminase activities. Fatty change and intrahepatic cholestasis is also common and produces elevation of plasma ALP and GGT activities. Figure 6.5 outlines the changes that may be associated with the more commonly used drugs. For detail the reader is referred to the further reading list.

Most agents have been described as occasionally producing liver damage. Drugs, or groups of drugs, with a high rate of hepatic involvement include:

- nitrosoureas;

- the antimetabolites e.g. cytosine arabinoside (cholestasis), methotrexate (cell damage);

- L-asparaginase produces diffuse fatty change in over half the patients in whom it is used. In addition to elevated bilirubin, transaminases and ALP, there is a decrease in the plasma concentrations of many proteins (albumin, transferrin, haptoglobin) and coagulation factors synthesised in the liver;

- combination chemotherapy;

- high dose chemotherapy preceding marrow transplant is associated, in about half the patients, with a potentially serious syndrome called veno-occlusive disease of the liver (see Figure 6.6). There is centrilobular cell necrosis and narrowing or fibrous obliteration of hepatic veins and sinusoids. Clinically it manifests as jaundice, painful hepatomegaly and fluid retention, usually with ascites and develops within 20 days. The mortality rate is up to 50% and a high plasma bilirubin concentration (>250 μmol/L) is a bad prognostic sign.

Pre-existing liver disease may impact on chemotherapy:

- drugs metabolised or excreted by the liver may require modification of the dose, if used at all;

- immunosuppressive therapy in a patient with viral hepatitis may permit viral replication. On withdrawal of therapy, the immune response to the virus may cause liver damage.

Drug	Liver cell damage	Cholestasis	Fatty Change	Other
Asparaginase	x		x	
Anabolic steroids		x		
Azathioprine	x	x		fibrosis
Busulphan	x		x	
Bleomycin			x	
Chlorambucil			x	
Cisplatin	x			
Cytosine arabinoside	x			
Cyclophosphamide	x			
5-Fluorouracil	x			
6-Mercaptopurine	x	x		
Methotrexate	x		x	fibrosis with chronic use
Vinblastine	x			

Figure 6.5   Changes induced in the liver by chemotherapeutic agents

Veno-occlusive disease

This 32 year old man had an embryonal carcinoma of the testis removed. Following surgery his plasma AFP values fell from 1232 to 322 kU/L but remained at this level. Bone marrow was collected and stored as a source of haemopoietic stem cells and chemotherapy begun. Two months later the AFP concentration was still elevated at 184 kU/L so it was decided to undertake high dose chemotherapy.

This consisted of a three day course of carboplatin, etoposide and ifosfamide. Four days later the previously harvested stem cells were infused. Over the next two weeks, the patient became jaundiced and developed an enlarged liver and ascites. This was considered to be due to veno-occlusive disease. The jaundice resolved and the patient was well two years later.

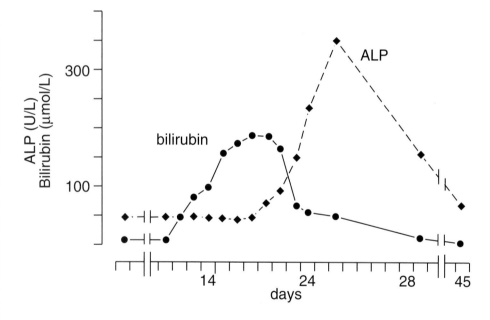

This shows the changes in plasma bilirubin (µmol/L) and alkaline phosphatase (U/L) over the days following high dose chemotherapy. Plasma transaminase activities rose only slightly. This pattern of changes is non-specific and may occur, for example, with sepsis. In this clinical context however, it supports the diagnosis of veno-occlusive disease.

Figure 6.6   Veno-occlusive disease

TUMOUR LYSIS SYNDROME

This is an uncommon, and largely preventable, consequence of cancer therapy which, if not recognised and treated early, may result in life-threatening side effects and death. The syndrome is typically seen during an initial cycle of chemotherapy when the malignant cells of bulky and rapidly growing cancers such as Burkitt's lymphoma, acute leukaemias and small cell lung cancer, suddenly undergo extensive necrosis and release their contents. The patient's biochemical profile (Figure 6.7) may change in a matter of hours with the onset of lactic acidosis accompanied by hyperuricemia leading to oliguria, and later anuria and acute tubular necrosis due to urate nephropathy. Plasma potassium and phosphate concentrations rise, calcium concentrations fall as a result of the rise in phosphate and cardiac tachyarrhythmias or sudden cardiac death may result. Release of cytoplasmic LD results in marked LD elevation.

The consequences of the tumour lysis syndrome can be largely prevented by pretreatment with allopurinol, which reduces urate formation, vigorous hydration and urinary alkalinization, and correction of hyperkalemia and other biochemical abnormalities, if necessary by renal dialysis. While the majority of cases of tumour lysis syndrome are observed in rapidly growing haematological neoplasms treated by chemotherapy, it may also occur following chemotherapy of solid tumours, radiation therapy and rarely following manipulation of bulky tumours during surgery. The syndrome is seen only infrequently during subsequent phases of treatment as the bulk of the tumour has by then been reduced.

Tumour lysis

This 83 year old man had polycythaemia vera for twelve years and then developed acute leukaemia with a white cell count (WCC) of 54 x 10⁹/L (4.0 - 10.0 x 10⁹/L).

Chemotherapy with daunorubicin and cytosine arabinoside was begun and allopurinol was administered. Despite this, the plasma urate rose as the tumour cells were destroyed and there was some impairment of renal function with the plasma creatinine rising from normal concentrations to 440 µmol/L (50 - 120).

This shows the typical changes of the tumour lysis syndrome.

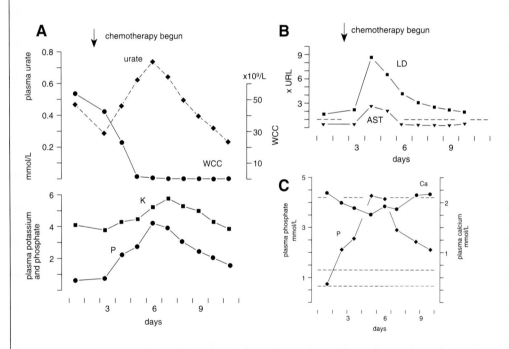

Note:
1. The relationship between the falling WCC (tumour mass) and plasma urate, potassium and phosphate from cells (A).
2. The rise in plasma enzyme activity (as multiple of the upper reference limit) due to cell destruction (B).
3. The relationship between plasma phosphate and calcium (C). The broken lines represent the reference interval for phosphate and the lower reference limit for calcium.

Figure 6.7   Tumour lysis

FURTHER READING

More detail on the topics discussed in this chapter should be sought in standard texts on oncology or pharmacology. Two useful ones are:

- Foley J F, Vose J M, Armitage J O. *Current therapy in cancer*. 1994. Philadelphia: WB Saunders Co.

- Perry M C (ed.). *The chemotherapy source book*. 1992. Baltimore: Williams and Wilkins.

Bearman S I. The syndrome of hepatic veno-occlusive disease after marrow transplantation. *Blood* 1995; 85: 3005-3020.

Perry M C. Chemotherapeutic agents and hepatotoxicity. *Sem Oncol* 1992; **19:** 551-65.

APPENDIX

DESCRIBING THE VALUE OF A TEST

In a population tested for a particular disease, a result above a defined cut-off value is positive, one below is negative. Then:

TP   true positives are those with the disease who are positive.

TN   true negatives are those without the disease who are negative.

FP   false positive are those without the disease who are positive.

FN   false negatives are those with the disease who are negative.

The sensitivity is
$$\frac{TP}{TP + FN} \times 100$$
(all with the disease)

and the specificity   is
$$\frac{TN}{TN + FP} \times 100$$
(all without the disease)

The predictive value of a positive result (PV (+ve)) is the percentage of positive results that are true positives.

$$PV\ (+ve) \quad = \quad \frac{TP}{TP + FP} \times 100$$

The predictive value of a negative result (PV(-ve)) is the percentage of negative results that are true negatives

$$PV (-ve) \quad = \quad \frac{TN}{FN + TN} \quad \times \; 100$$

The efficiency of a test is defined by the percentage of correct results.

$$PV (-ve) \quad = \quad \frac{TN}{FN + TN} \quad \times \; 100$$

For further information see: Galen R S, Gambino S R. Beyond normality. The predictive value and efficiency of medical diagnoses 1979. New York: John Wiley and Sons, Inc.

Index

D

E

F

G

R